CW00971286

Sandra Hoffmann lives in Munich, where she teaches creative writing at the Literaturhaus as well as at the universities of Augsburg and Karlsruhe. She also writes for radio and newspapers, and is an avid surfer. Her novel *Was ihm fehlen wird, wenn er tot ist* (Hanser Berlin, 2012) won her the Thaddäus Troll Prize, followed by the Hans Fallada Prize for *Paula* (Hanser Berlin, 2017). Her most recent publication is her first book for young adults, *Das Leben spielt hier* (Hanser, 2019).

Katy Derbyshire was born in London and has lived in Berlin for over twenty years. She is an award-winning translator of contemporary German writers, including Olga Grjasnowa, Angela Steidele and Clemens Meyer. Having taught literary translation in New York, New Delhi and Norwich, she now co-hosts a monthly translation lab and the bi-monthly Dead Ladies Show in Berlin. Katy is the publisher of the V&Q Books imprint.

Paula
by Sandra Hoffmann

The translation of this work was supported by a grant from the Goethe-Institut in the framework of the 'Books First' programme.

V&Q Books, Berlin 2020
An imprint of Verlag Voland & Quist GmbH
First published in Germany as *Paula* in 2017 by Hanser Berlin
Copyright © 2017 Hanser Berlin in der Carl Hanser Verlag GmbH
& Co. KG, Munich.
Translation copyright © Katy Derbyshire 2020
Editing: Florian Duijsens
Copy editing: Alyson Coombes
Cover design: Pingundpong*Gestaltungsbüro
Typesetting: Fred Uhde
Printing and binding: PBtisk, Příbram, Czech Republic

www.vq-books.eu

Paula

by Sandra Hoffmann

Translated from the German by Katy Derbyshire

'Do you know nothing? Do you see nothing? Do you remember nothing?'

T. S. Eliot, *The Waste Land*

We have a word in German: *schweigen*. It means deliberately remaining silent; it is different to merely being quiet. *Schweigen* offers nothing to hold on to, not even if you reach deep into your pockets for a coin to flip between your fingers, or a shopping list on a scrap of paper. You hear, from somewhere else or from inside yourself, the dark sounds of muteness turning against you; you hear them as rumbling, as murmuring, as ongoing grumbling, muttering, somewhere far away and yet also near. As though all the unspoken words were seeking ways out of that mute body and into the room, forging their way to you. They rob you of your peace and of your sleep. *Schweigen*, when someone lives close beside you and remains so silent, swallows down every word so unrelentingly that there is nothing left over, not for you or anyone else. *Schweigen*, at the table when the knives and forks scrape against plates, when someone, just one voice, says: Could you pass the salt, please? And someone else passes it. And above it all, that deliberate silence that seems to eat you up, you and all your good summers and your few good winters. As though joy itself might never return. And you hear the sound of stockinged legs moving under the table and the dog brushing past a chair, a cough or a throat muscle constricting as glugs of water go down. When the sounds of bodies have occupied so much space that there's nothing but density in the room, a buffer against the outside world. That deliberate silence ends up trapped in every crack of a house; it radiates, emanates, makes a house into a fortress, and the only possible release is a drastic end. You can stay and die, or you can leave. In that quiet, though, even a tractor outside in the road would be a beautiful sound, a promise, someone mowing the field for the first time in the year, the day still light. The world would be there again. Bright light and language.

My grandmother Paula died on 10 November 1997 at the age of 82. She never talked about herself, not to the very end. She took her whole life to the grave, all her secrets and all her troubles.

When I run through the park in the morning, jog around the lake and hear the swans and waterfowl, when I watch the mandarin ducks, luminous like bright dots among the other birds, I often think of my grandmother, dead for 18 years now, and I think of my parents. I'd like to show them the park, the dogs I pass regularly on my run, the lovely spots on the side streams of the Eisbach, the water's surface occasionally brushed by willows. The men face-down on the ground next to their personal trainers, doing complicated gymnastic manoeuvres, or hitting a small punch bag suspended from a tree over and over and over, to make them feel strong for whatever reason. I'd like to show them the yogis saluting the sun, the Japanese woman swinging her arms oddly as she walks. I see the surfers on the Eisbach wave, and sometimes I stop to watch them. I watch these strangers and I'm glad of them, glad I can weave my way between them and, without speaking to them, I know: I'm happy that they're here. I'd like to say to my family: Look, this is where I live now. This is how my life has turned out, and it's fine. But my grandmother is dead. And my parents aren't really interested in any lives not directly related to theirs. I talk to them as I run; I show them my world in my mind, and it always makes me sad.

That deliberate silence has been passed down the generations.

1915 was the year of the wood rabbit in the Chinese calendar. The German politician Franz Josef Strauss was born, Ingrid Bergman, Edith Piaf too, Frank Sinatra, Pinochet. It was the second year of the First World War; the first International Women's Peace Congress was held in The Hague; Albert Einstein talked publicly about his theory of relativity; and Virginia Woolf published her debut novel. Paula was born on All Hallows Day, the first of November, in a small village in the middle of Catholic Upper Swabia. She was her parents' first child. The conditions Paula was born into were modest; her family did not have much money. She grew up with two sisters and a brother, who died on the front in the Second World War. She did talk about his death. Over and over, more often than I wanted to hear it.

He died, in the war.

That was Paula's story. Five words long.

When she died, it was the end of the story of a woman I know little about. She experienced a world war, gave birth to two children. She profited from Germany's postwar boom, but never learned a trade and was like a guest worker in her own country. Cleaning lady was the name of the job she did. Sometimes I can sense her voice. I listen to her like I listened to her sister Marie; she is dead now too. I listen to her like I listened to my mother, who has long since stopped talking about her mother's deliberate silence. I hear all their voices; they don't cohere, they come and go; they like to hide. When I get too close to them they flee; that's how it seems, anyway. I think it might be possible to tell Paula's life story with their help. I want to get to the bottom of it.

She was my grandmother.

I am an unreliable narrator. I've done talking therapy. I've reflected on my life. I've tried to trace the paths I've taken, to understand the past storms inside of me so that I can weather the storms to come. I have got good at all that. You can rely on me in that respect. Yes, you can rely on me to make up everything I no longer know, everything I've never known, everything I have to know – put it all on the page. How else might it be possible to unfold what I never knew alongside what I still know very well? How can a writer tell a story that returns over and over in her dreams – nightmares or fears or dark forebodings that extend all the way to my present life? How can I tell a story that darts up in the form of an image in the daytime, and then darts away again? And how can I say why I haven't been to the cemetery for seven years now – or only once, secretly.

One thing I don't have to make up: the way the skin of my grandmother's face felt, like a violet's petal, almost translucent, like it had never been touched. No furrows meandered along it, nothing but fine lines, signs, traces, like birds leave behind in the snow. And I still know her scent. Warm and not sour. Mild and not coarse. Her smell was better than she was. Softer, gentler. She never smelled old. When I want to, I can still feel that warm grandmotherly body and the wall with the woodchip wallpaper. I can see myself lying between them, on those nights after I had bad dreams. The rosary moves between my grandmother's hands, and she lights consecrated candles. Sometimes my face brushes against hers.

I love you and I hate you – children never say both in one sentence. Children say one or the other. 'I love you' is not a line from my childhood. But neither is 'I hate you'. Nothing was clear-cut, other than our fear of dying. And at some point, I refused to let my grandmother take my hand.

In a drawer in her room, underneath the hymnals with or without gilt edging and all manner of little booklets and cards depicting the saints, she kept a brightly coloured chocolate box, a sturdy straw box and a probably homemade blue album with red and white embroidery on the front cover. All three were full of photos. Pictures of people of various ages, a great many men, some of them soldiers. Men on motorcycles, a man with a car, men in a field, men alongside ships, beside tanks, by forests and roadsides, men's names on crosses. Men with men in fancy cars. More rarely, men with women in cars. Some of the men are wearing work outfits that I recognise from documentaries about forced labourers. Many of them are in uniform. There are men in elegant suits, men with ties and bowties, men with monocles, smart men in casual clothing. Dark-skinned men in uniform too, presumably Moroccan men, almost certainly in fact. Men with happy faces, priests, black and white priests in robes. Altar boys. My father, beaming and handsome at his wedding to my beautiful mother. No real family photos, apart from pictures of families I've never seen before. Women. Paula's sisters: Marie and Theresia. The three sisters with a child. Theresia's daughter. Theresia's daughter and my mother. My grandmother Paula with an inflatable rubber ring in a lake. Paula next to a handsome man in a meadow, long white gloves that match her flowered dress, Paula with the same man on a large motorcycle, Paula at the grave of a man who was once her bridegroom-to-be, Paula and five other women at a kitchen table, cheerful. Women in groups, lined up like a gymnastics team. Paula with her mother, Paula with an unknown woman and unknown children. And so on. Paula at her daughter's wedding, looking at the fairy-tale bride: dark, joyless, the eyes the darkest things in her stern face. Paula with a handbag in a flowery meadow, her gaze sombre, clutching ox-eye daisies. Her grey bun tightly wound. One leg bandaged beneath her suit. Next to her, my mother in a pencil skirt, back-combed short hair and sunglasses, rather Audrey Hepburnesque as always and striding along a country path in heels like it's the Champs-Élysées. I spot myself, a girl with a boy's haircut in a green dress, not flirting with the camera. My grandmother Paula on the leather sofa with Marie, my mother and me. My mother looking like she's come straight out of the pages of a chic young fashion magazine, palazzo pants, a blouse that would be from ETRO these days, her hair, her painted fingernails. She is 26 and so gorgeous I can't take my eyes off her. And then I see it: my mother feels out of place. I see her dark, melancholy eyes, I see that she's not present. And I see Paula and Marie taking care of me, the child with the doll and the badly cut hair, an exception to the rule. They're taking care, as always. I'm six years old in the photograph. I know that because my hair was longer at seven and eight: my shiny mid-length Cilla Black hair that I was only allowed for a while. Wearing real clogs and a denim pinafore dress on the island of Isola Bella in Lago Maggiore, I was allowed to be a girl who was not second to her mother. After that, my hair was cut again.

My grandmother was born in a village called Assmannshardt, which had ceased to exist after the Thirty

Years' War that devastated 17th-century Central Europe. All its inhabitants had died of murder, pillage, starvation, plague or rape, and then the village was burnt down. For whatever reason, new settlers came from the Montafon valley and Vorarlberg, on the other side of Lake Constance. My grandmother grew up in that village. Her own mother was a strict, cold woman, my mother says, but in the photos I have seen of her she looks gentle and that makes her seem young, although she must have been very old by the time they were taken. Paula's father, my mother's grandfather, lived a long life and was the most adorable person you could imagine, my mother says. Good cop, bad cop, that's what I say. He was her substitute father, that's what she says, and: What would she have done without him? Her life would have been impossible but for him.

There is no order in the photo boxes. There are pictures upon pictures, hundreds, some small, some slightly larger, some that look as though they've been flipped and turned countless times, and others yellowed but apparently untouched. There are several copies of some, as if they'd been intended as gifts to others. And inevitably, the photos begin to lead lives of their own in my thoughts, turning to me behind Paula's back, saying: You can tell us any story you want. We're here.

They are seducers. They pretend to reveal all willingly, but they remain resistant. Wordless. Paper.

And if I had asked my grandmother for permission?

She wasn't a storyteller, she was a woman who prayed, a woman who remained immersed in herself; she wouldn't have answered. She would have said no by not saying yes.

She explained the Rosary prayer and its five decades to me while her rosary beads lay on the table, not moving. She told me when each of the Rosary Mysteries are said and when to say the Joyful Mysteries and when the Sorrowful. I would always forget.

She herself prayed countless times a day and I'm sure at night as well. Her hand would move in her apron pocket like a small creature, unwilling to show itself at work. Yet the rosary is nothing but a string of beads with a cross on it. No more and no less. Though that's not quite true. The number of beads is fixed, as is how to pray the Rosary and when. And if you believe in it, it helps, she would say. Someone's watching from up above, and He means well when you're good. He forgives everything if only you turn to Him enough, she would say. Life and God's love both depend on how much, how often and how well you pray. That's how I understood it as a child. If you pray the wrong way you're at risk. If you don't pray enough, you're more likely to die. If you don't pray your sins away, you're in big trouble. So I prayed too. Prayed that I'd wake up again the next day when the day had been good, and that I'd wake up again the next day when the day had been bad, because I'd secretly thought bad thoughts about someone and secretly said bad words. It was possible to pray without a rosary, in bed at night, my legs drawn up under me, my body bent over them, the crown of my head against the wall; in yoga, it's called Child's Pose. At confession, it meant 20 Our Fathers, 20 Hail Marys, contemplation during both, and between them my requests for forgiveness, for *His* forgiveness. I prayed that I'd wake up again in case I fell asleep and hadn't prayed enough, and that my mother and father and brother wouldn't die.

I never knew whether God saw or heard me, I just didn't want my grandmother to die. I wanted her to leave me alone with her prayers, which she claimed to pray for me when really, she was praying against her fears. Later, I wanted her to die. And once I stopped wishing her dead, she did die.

What makes a person? And how can a woman add up, build up to a real live individual if she's done her utmost to reveal nothing of herself? Her voice, to find out what her voice adds up to, you have to imagine yourself so close you can feel her, hear it, her inner murmur, her silent conversation, her thinking through prayer. Groping for understanding, it is impossible to get close enough if you don't start with your own memories. It is impossible to invent the truth. Precision is essential. Fiction is the only way to close the gaps between image and image, fragment and fragment. Enduring the constant fractures in memory, the breaks in our relationship, as though she could still say: No, I won't give you permission. No, you may not know me. No, you may not tell my story. How far do vetoes extend? How far does silence reach? She refuses, even in my memory, vetoes me inventing her, Paula, beyond death itself. The commandment to stay silent. And then: how words can be forged out of what has been silenced.

If we were to sit around a table, tell each other stories, happy and sad, talk and talk for nights and nights, perhaps then a life would build itself up?

But Paula's life remained silenced, and that deliberate silence stole into our family's life like a virus, passed on from one person to another, from one generation to the next.

And you thought – not only as a child, but later too – perhaps only animals feel at home in these silent parts of the world. Perhaps their bodies make paths for themselves, perhaps their fur protects them. Perhaps it's their different language. The mewling and grunting, the yowling and barking, and the way birds sound in spring, in summer, the way they grow quieter in winter. You suspect that some animals transform deliberate silence into silent speech, and that some have no effect at all on the human world.

I am seven years old. I'm balancing on the wall, trying not to tread on any moss. If you tread on moss, you die and fall into a grave. It's not a game: from my great-grandparents' grave, I balance along the wall over to the water tank, pump the handle a few times and drink out of the iron tap. Then I pump another three times. Water runs into the trough. The sound is lovely. Three is a good number. A safe number. I walk back along the wall. I'm only allowed to do that when no one else is at the cemetery. The moss on the wall is black and brown and yellow and red. Only green in places.

Why is that? I asked my grandmother, but she didn't give me an answer.

It's to do with the age of the moss, my Uncle Gustl said.

After counting to 20 exactly nine times as I balance and once to three, I get to the grave. I can look down on the grave from the wall.

My mother says there's a child in the grave as well. He doesn't have a name. He's underneath my great-grandmother and great-grandfather.

Why doesn't he have a name?

The baby had a split spine, my mother says, and she says it was Auntie Marie who told her, my grandmother's sister. It might have been her other sister, though, Theresia.

What does that look like, I wonder, is the spine not closed, does it reveal everything inside the person like in diagrams of the human body in school textbooks?

Why didn't he grow properly? I ask.

All sorts of things happen, my mother says. If you have a split spine you also have damage to your brain.

The boy who would have been my mother's brother must've had brain damage then.

They have the same stubborn streak, Paula and her sister Marie. When they don't want to speak, they don't speak. They wear the same brightly patterned aprons they did 20 years ago, as though they were still living in their village, where everything was dirty. Our house is not dirty. Auntie Marie and her husband give us all kinds of things; it doesn't matter whether we have done anything or not done anything to deserve it. My brother and I are their godchildren and they do everything for us, having no children of their own. From Auntie Marie and her husband Gustl, I learned the names of animals and how to stroke deer. We visited all the animal parks and all the adventure playgrounds within a day's reach of their Goggomobil microcar, as long as we could get back before dark. I learned the names of flowers and stones from them, and how the Swabian Alps came to be. And I learned to understand the family's soft but impenetrable Swabian dialect. I learned how to tell the difference between clay, limestone and marl.

I'm on the back seat of the Goggo car with my Auntie Marie next to me, and whenever my uncle talks to us, my aunt says, Eyes on the road! She doesn't seem to see that he's not looking at us, or only in the rear-view mirror, where he winks at me through his thick glasses. From the back seat, the countryside outside looks just like our dear Lord always wanted it to be, as my Oma Paula would say, but thankfully she's not with us this time. Auntie Marie smells of 4711 cologne and I don't think it smells awful, but I don't like it when she hugs me because I don't want to smell like her. I'm wearing my green dress with the long sleeves and the white trim; I'm growing out of the dress because children grow a lot between the ages of six and seven, before they start school. The dress is too warm for a cloudless day in the Goggomobil. I look out of the window, and although everything looks so beautiful I'm not happy. Not cheerful and carefree. I'm scared something might happen because I've thought a bad thing, and I mustn't think it or say it again, and if I don't start praying right now it will happen. I can recite the Lord's Prayer and the Hail Mary as easily as my bedtime prayer. I try not to murmur as I pray, staring out of the window and thinking the prayer mutely to myself, because no one needs to know, because it's my secret. If I manage the Lord's Prayer twice without interruption, nothing will happen. He is very much concerned with my sins. The Virgin Mother is concerned with my hopes. Sometimes I hope for things that aren't nice, so then there's not much difference.

But now I hear my aunt saying: Look at that huge tree, and I nod and don't let her distract me.

Look, black cows, says my aunt, and I've already managed one Our Father.

Have you ever seen cows that black? Auntie Marie says, and I can't answer or I won't manage it. I nod and she says: Really?

And from the front seat my uncle says: Of course, last time we came this way.

I continue my prayer, that's good, while looking at the cows out of the Goggomobil window, pretending to concentrate on them, though they don't disappear very fast, because a Goggo doesn't go very fast.

Oh, I forgot that, my aunt says. Of course, yes, you have seen them before.

I nod.

She strokes my hair, which my mother has had cut short again because it's more practical, though it would make me look like a boy if I weren't wearing a dress. My mother says I should have been a boy anyway, plus all the women in Paris look like that. My mother worships Parisian women and looks a little bit like them herself. I take a deep breath once I've finished.

I say: I've seen the cows before.

Their fur's as black as yours, says Auntie Marie.

I don't have fur, I say. I have hair.

My uncle laughs and my aunt strokes my hair again. I can't relax.

Why doesn't Oma have an Opa? I ask. I've been thinking about it for a long time. If I formulate it like this it's not a bad thought. It's better for me not to think there aren't any men who like my Oma. I've worked it all out.

My Auntie Marie strokes my hair much faster now, like she trying to iron out the curls, and then she says: It didn't turn out that way.

And my uncle says: You've got us.

But Mummy hasn't got a daddy, I say. I remember those words to this day, and the response too.

She does, my uncle said. He was a gypsy!

A gap is a blank space, and it may well stay that way, impossible to close, even with the best will in the world. Because no one knows the missing variable, no one has the fingerprint that solves the mystery, the PIN, the PUK. Because there's no formula and no password: one of the two people whose cells you carry inside you remains a nobody. Nameless, stateless, no picture or passport, no father's name on your mother's birth certificate. A person, a man, about whom only one thing is certain: he wasn't pale-skinned or blond, and he wasn't black either. And for this reason, or because you sense you carry something inside you that you don't know, you stare at it, this nothingness that you wish would reveal its mystery, that you keep twisting and turning, that you circle like hyenas circle their prey. First you ask questions, then you fantasise. A lot of things are possible, but not everything.

As old ladies, they often go to church together, my Auntie Marie and Paula, my grandmother. I don't think they talk to each other much, but when they do talk, it's mainly Marie. At least, I suspect so. When I see the two of them from behind, which happens quite often because I follow them on roller skates, Marie is slimmer and Paula bulkier; they walk in sync, their handbags in the crook of their right elbows. One blue-grey head of hair and one brown, never turning to face each other, and when their arms happen to touch as they walk, they move a little further apart. After they turn the corner down the hill, they're gone. I stay put at the top of the curve, watching them until they vanish at the next bend in the road, beside the farmhouse. I am free. Nobody is watching me now. I fly along the road on my skates.

Like my grandmother, I enjoy sitting by the window, and like my grandmother, I enjoy looking out at nature. I enter a state of peace that makes me wish she also got to experience moments like these. Sometimes, at least. I hear her saying: Can you see the squirrel? Can you see the yellow butterfly? And: Does that farmer have to make so much noise at this time of day? I hear her speaking her language. Her Swabian dialect, in which the sentence about the farmer is: *Muos der um dia Zeit no so 'n Krach macha.* I hear her saying the simplest things in the world, but they mean a lot because they were the only things she talked about. Everything else, she kept to herself. It is for her that I hear the cock crowing and for her I see laundry fluttering on a windy day. I hear her saying: Come, stay a while longer. It's possible on the terrace and by the window that looks out over the lawn. It's only possible when we, my grandmother Paula and I, are watching nature, looking at animals. They break the silence. It's impossible, even today impossible in my mind, to sit next to her at the table unless we're deeply engrossed in a meal, impossible to sit next to her on the sofa unless *Bonanza* is on. I instantly descend into sinister thoughts, my words grind to a halt, I lose my voice. If I get too close to her I usually can't write about her any more.

When I lean back, I can at least watch her in the motions of the cherry tree's leaves. From a distance – then there's peace.

Sometimes they sit next to each other on the sofa, but they still avoid touching each other. Marie has come to visit with Gustl, her husband, who's a great joker, but my grandmother can't stand jokes. She doesn't talk to Gustl. Perhaps she can't stand men in general these days. All three of them are sitting on our sofa, and Gustl is talking to my father and now and then to me or my brother, and Auntie Marie talks to me or my brother as well, and she keeps her hands folded on her lap. She's not praying. I know she isn't. I can spot it straight away by now. Marie is like a buzzard. My grandmother is like an owl, only becoming a buzzard seeking her prey at night or when no one is there. My mother is barely speaking. She likes talking to Gustl best. She thinks his jokes are funny. We children think it's funny when he says *com-pooter*, like he doesn't know better; when he mispronounces the footballer's name as *Rummerige*, even though he's his biggest hero on the pitch. My grandmother has one hand in her apron pocket. When the buzzard next to her spots the mouse, the mouse holds still. My grandmother remains deliberately silent.

You remember Tamara, the pigeon that landed in the garden with an injured wing. She came as a sign. She wasn't carrying a letter from a grandfather, but it was certainly possible that she should have been, it was certainly possible that she had been, that the letter had got lost along the way. Animals don't speak, but Tamara tapped out signals with her beak, Morse code, possibly from another country, you told your friends and anyone who'd listen. A carrier pigeon doesn't just come to you by chance. It has a task and a destination. This pigeon's deliberate silence was a good silence, it was a sign of a mystery that would be easy to work out, as long as you made an effort. With animals, it's easy to say you know what they're thinking and doing. It's up to you to interpret them.

There is a day when my grandmother isn't silent for once, when Saint Nicholas and his manservant Knecht Ruprecht have come to see us. I'm sitting under the low living-room table next to her sturdy thighs, next to her bandaged leg, which is always poorly without anyone knowing what's wrong with it, and I look out at their two pairs of boots and have no idea yet that Saint Nicholas is the boss and Ruprecht is only his assistant. Ruprecht has a whole year's bad deeds in his knapsack; he's written them down for every child and he has a willow switch with him too. He can beat children, and he will. He'll do it exactly the same way as Sister Soteris with her brush at kindergarten and my father with his bare hand. Only it will hurt more because the big switch he's brought along hits harder.

But nothing will happen if you're good, my father said.

I'm not always good. I have bad thoughts and I ate raspberries from the neighbour's garden without asking and I want to take little Bernd's toy car away from him.

Thou shalt not covet, my grandmother says, and Sister Soteris says the same.

If all else fails, I bite. I only bite when I have to or when I feel rejected. I bite my little brother as well. Knecht Ruprecht doesn't do anything to grown-ups, even if they smack their children's bottoms. I'm sitting under the table next to my grandmother's fat calves and I can see the suspenders under her skirt, but I've seen them plenty of times before so they don't distract me. I'm trembling. I don't want to be seen, not for anything in the world, and I don't want to be beaten. I'm crying, but only so no one can hear. I cry as quietly as I can, scarcely daring to breathe.

I hear there's a good little girl here who always goes to kindergarten, the voice says.

My grandmother says: That's very true.

I hear there's a good little girl here who always tidies her things.

I wait.

My grandmother, sadly, doesn't react as quickly this time, but then she says: That's right.

I hear a nice little girl lives here.

Yes, she does, says my grandmother.

And where is this little girl? the voice asks.

I tremble even more, and because I'm trembling so much I bump my head on the underside of the table and there's a loud noise, and my leg slips and pokes out from under the table for a moment, and I pull it right back in, but my leg is trembling so hard that it hits the table leg and the melamine table almost collapses.

Why won't the little girl come out? asks the voice.

Sadly my grandmother says nothing now.

I count very slowly, because I can only count up to 10, and when I get to four, the voice says: Can't we coax the little girl out?

No, my grandmother says instantly. She'll stay where she is.

After liberation from the Nazis, the Vorarlberg region and the southern part of Upper Swabia, including Assmannshardt and the more southerly areas on the German side of Lake Constance, were occupied by the French, including Moroccan soldiers. They were loved and hated. They brought both salvation and damnation. In my grandmother's brightly patterned box, I find a photograph of three beaming men standing by a river, presumably the Danube. Two of them have very dark skin and are wearing uniforms; the third, lighter-skinned than the others, wears work clothing. He is pointing at the photographer. I think I can make out something in his face that I also spot in my mother's face in early photos: close-set eyes, a strong nose, similar facial contours, radiant eyes. A radiance that comes from sadness. I might be wrong. There is no proof for anything.

So perhaps everything is completely different, and her child isn't descended from a Pole as I first thought but from a Moroccan. Fatima, Berber. My beautiful mother.

More and more, when I look in the mirror or at photos, I recognise my mother's face in my own. The lines around the mouth, those thin feathered wrinkles on the sides of the chin I don't like. In none of the pictures I have of my mother do I recognise my grandmother's face in hers. They have no similar lines or wrinkles. The paternal influence on my mother's appearance was significant. I search all male faces for my mother's face.

And then I find myself holding this photograph, Paula as a young girl next to her mother Josephine, and I see that they could be sisters, were they not 20 or 25 years apart. And if they were sisters, they would be the kind fresh out of the woods, where they are never scared; not impressionable Red Riding Hoods but girls, women, who dared. There is no fear in their faces. No trace of the fear I later so often read on my grandmother's face.

There is one photo of my grandmother and her two sisters sitting at the edge of a field, laughing. And I see that it's the way they're sitting, their posture and perhaps the eyes that makes them similar. But there's a little girl between my grandmother's sisters who doesn't share that similarity, and although I don't know who that child is – it's not my mother – I'm interested in this strange child between the cheerful sisters, this girl in a white-aproned Sunday frock, a bow in her hair, because there's fear on her face, because she sees something she doesn't like. She has to look, even though she wants to look away, and perhaps she does like it after all. And then I see that only my grandmother and the girl are looking in the same direction, to where the camera is, where the photographer is standing, where there must be something as amusing as it is frightening, and I think of animals. I think of a man with a monkey, a man with a camel, a man with a parrot, a man with a lion. And although my favourite thought is that the sisters spot a lion, that lion seems very unlikely. Not from looking at the girl's face, but at my grandmother's face, her sisters' faces. In their faces, a monkey is dancing the tango or a parrot is singing a funny song. I wonder what a photograph is capable of capturing other than an instant, other than people in one moment, experiencing an emotion, an encounter, a connection? What does the photograph give me other than the certainty that my grandmother, her sisters, their parents and all the others already existed when I didn't exist yet? What does a photograph tell me if I don't force a narrative onto the depicted situation, the landscape and the figures? The girl is afraid. The sisters are laughing. All four of them know each other. The field rises to a hill. It is spring. The flowers are the key to that.

The doll's pram was the best thing she owned, and the doll was the best doll anyone could own at the time; so proud, she guarded and tended her prize possession, my mother says. And I listen mutely and look at the photograph, a picture of a girl, a child outside a house so ramshackle and rotten that it looks as though it might collapse at any moment. In front of that small house, the graceful dark-skinned girl stands in the snow, proud and shy and a little bit enchanted to be holding the doll's pram, which I recognise because it was in our cellar for years, because it was sacred, because it looked so beautiful that it must have come from a real palace, belonged to a real princess. And I know the doll inside the pram, sitting upright and perhaps in a traditional skirt and apron. I know that doll, whose hair I once cut off because I thought the doll was like me; its hair felt like human hair. It will grow back, I thought. Someone had implanted real hair in the porcelain head and never dreamed there would one day be a child with a pair of scissors who wanted the doll to look like her, with short hair and a bit like a boy. And my mother freezing when she sees what's happened, and then beginning to tell the sad story of a girl who didn't have much apart from a dog and the doll and the princess doll's pram made of thickly varnished woven plastic in an elegant eggshell white with a detachable hood to protect against the sun, with its enamel and rubber wheels. I was the same age as you are now, my mother says. And how impossible it is not to cry, because I'm so ashamed of myself.

My mother says she's put it behind her long ago. She says she's lived a good life. You can keep the photos, I don't want them, she says. There's nothing we can find out now anyway, she says. None of them will talk, she says. Them, at that point, is my great-aunt Marie, who is still alive. She's never said anything, says my mother. It's true. When I write a novel about the Polish forced labourer who might have been her father, it upsets my mother; a novel about a person neither of us knows, neither of us has ever seen; we don't even know his name; a novel about a person who appears from my grandmother's photographs, nothing but conjecture. When my mother reads the novel, she can't sleep for a few nights. Once she's finished she calls me, tells me about the hard work, the pain, but also the happiness that the story triggered in her, and in the end she asks me a question: How do you know him so well?

I laugh; it's the best compliment you can get about an imaginary character.

I made up a person. It takes more than two years for Janek Biliński to leave me – the imaginary character who seems so possible, so real to me.

Even though my father and brother live in our house too, the women decide everything. My grandmother Paula and my mother stick to each other like mating fire bugs, but actually they can't stand living together. I want to understand that. I sense the discomfort in every cranny of the house, I hear words where there are none, and I have to stay watchful in order to stand it. I have bad dreams at night. It was this way when I was five, 14, and it will be the same later in life. In my memory, years mix with other years. Fears mix with other fears. My fear of burglars with my grandmother's fear when I was a girl that something might happen to me. The fear of poisonous plants with the fear that my bad thoughts will kill a member of my family. The fear of dying is the most devastating fear, but sometimes that too merges together with another fear.

Thunder sets in. Outside, gorgeous clouds pile up, the sky's masses overlapping and interweaving grey on grey, and I look out of the dormer window, filled with awe. My grandmother walks around our floor of the house and pulls out all the plugs. The TV gets unplugged. Downstairs, my mother does the same, because fear is infectious. I watch the lightning flash in the distance, listen to the thunder in the distance, and it could be so wonderful. My grandmother lights candles, consecrated ones, I know, because other candles are no use against storms and death and the devil. She lights candles everywhere, and then it's allowed: she begins to pray, because we're only protected from what's gathering up there in the sky when we pray. She tells me I have to close the window; it'll be starting soon. I want to see it starting, I want to count how many seconds pass between thunder and lightning like my father taught me, but she says it's dangerous. I can feel the fear in the room, the fear with its particular smell. My grandmother often smells of fear. Outside where the storm is raging is where life is, and where we are is fear. I'm caught in the middle, and if I want to get out, it either has to be good weather or I have to burrow deep into myself. But even there it's not safe any more. Dangers lurk inside me, especially bad thoughts. How old I was at that point doesn't matter now; 10 or 11 or 12. We're already living in the house where nothing gets better.

Is that my Opa?
No.
This one then?
She says nothing. I elbow her. Hmm? Is that him? That's him, isn't it?
She shakes her head.
Why won't you tell me?
We're sitting on her sofa. I'm not all that small any more and we're looking at the photos again, the ones that live in the drawer with my baby pictures. I like being told what I was like as a baby, so I often take the red album out of the drawer and every time I do, I see another album and the photos in the boxes. My grandmother doesn't want me taking them out, just like she doesn't want to answer now. I can tell she wants to get up, so I lean against her all the more. It's warm underneath her wing. I look up and see her looking at the photo of the man smiling.
Is that him? I ask.
She slams the blue album shut. You've got homework to do, she says. I know she knows that's not true. Afternoons are for homework. It's almost time for *Bonanza* now.
My grandmother levers herself off the sofa, takes the album and says: That's enough now.
But why, Oma? I ask. She leaves the room.
Two minutes later, I follow. I heard her going into the bathroom. I wait outside the door. I can't hear anything. Then I hear rustling. In a loud voice, I say: Why won't you tell me?

I can't possibly wait until she comes out of the bathroom. It seems to take ages. I go downstairs to my mother and brother. I don't care if I miss *Bonanza*. Oma can fall down the toilet for all I care.

My mother and brother are in the living room.

The table is laid for dinner but my father's not home yet.

What's the matter? my mother asks.

Nothing, I say, because my mother always tells me not to ask people so many questions.

Before I fall asleep, I have to say a lot of prayers because of my bad wish.

I've done it countless times before and I do it again now. I put the photograph of the three dark-skinned men from my grandmother's box next to my mother's communion photo. It's a picture in which anyone can see how different my mother looks, how unlike the rest of her family, the rest of the village, the other children in her class at school, who I only know from photos. I look at the mouth of the man whose skin is lighter, transfixed by him because he's pointing his index finger at me, the observer – in reality probably at the photographer – and he's smiling; I'm transfixed by how he's smiling. I try to focus on his eyes and then I switch my gaze to the picture of my mother. I'm certain it's their eyes. The white of them, the stark contrast to the iris, the depth, the shape. The asymmetry of the eyes and brows, only noticeable on closer inspection. It's their mouths, it's the shape of their noses. It's the forehead.

It's clear, my husband says, it's certainly clear there are a lot of similarities.

33

My mother was born in the September of the year after the war. My Auntie Marie cradles her, a delicate child, and Marie's eyes are affectionate. Marie herself will never have children.

She tells us she lived with the animals, with her grandfather and the dog, a spitz. She says that she was the child who didn't belong there, that a single room for herself would have been enough. A bed and a bedside table and a chair and a wardrobe. A window facing the woods. A door to close behind her. She tells us that it was always this way, that her mother gave her nothing but orders. How coldness feels, how a mother can be without warmth, how a mother can smell bad, how you don't want to be near your own mother, or you do because you believe everything has to get better at some point. How it would be if you didn't even believe that any more. She tells us you'd believe it anyway. She tells us you can't understand it if you haven't been through it. That you'd do anything, at 15, so as not to be there all day long, in a house where there's nothing but hope that one day will be the day you finally learn something. Something good. How that expectation of good changes, over a lifetime, into its opposite. Like her tone of voice, my mother's face is bitter as she tells us all this. We want nice stories, we children, but there aren't many nice stories. There is what there is: the animals in the garden that take the place of people, the plums, the apples and pears and berries, and the sledges from those snowy winters that went faster than any new one. The description of a dog, repeated a hundred times over in all school holidays and at bedtimes: Tell me about the spitz! How the dog becomes our own first dog, as though he were real. How our mother's grandfather becomes our grandfather too, because we children never had one. How generous of heart, how noble the man was. That's what she tells us.

My grandfather's name was Elizius Haberbosch and he was a snail. That's the first story I make up for other children. So he does exist, my grandfather. I'm still at primary school. I start collecting snails, I start picking snails off steps and paths, from fields about to be mown, I start saving snails from people, and I will keep on doing this for the rest of my life.

We're on holiday near Saintes-Maries-de-la-Mer and my mother loves going to markets. As we stroll across the large square with its stalls, a Roma woman approaches my mother to read her palm; she says it shows everything about her, including where she comes from. Fear in my mother's eyes. She looks at my father. She shakes her head, determined. No, she says, and then she strides away. She never wants to go to that market again, she never wants to go anywhere again where she might come across 'gypsies'. She never wants to come back to Saintes-Maries-de-la-Mer.

There's a photograph of me at about 30, where I look very like that Roma woman from the market. So many Roma women want to read my palm. Two men love you, one of them once told me. It's not all that bad, Mum.

Why won't you stop pestering me with your questions? says my Auntie Marie. Why won't it ever stop?

Several times in my life, I have been taken for Greek, Moroccan, Turkish, half-Indian, French or Italian. I'm still looking for the root that feeds these assumptions. Where does my skin colour come from, my dark wires of hair? You can find out what country your father originates from, you can decode your DNA's genealogy by getting your spit tested, my brother-in-law tells me, and he says he knows someone who can help me. I ponder it for a while, but in the end, I ask myself: What would it change if my grandfather was not the 'gypsy' but a Moroccan, or not a Polish forced labourer but a Moroccan, or not a Moroccan or a Pole or a gypsy but a dark-skinned priest from Lord knows where? He too is in my grandmother's photos. The deliberate silence would not be broken, and my grandfather would not be found.

It's not my mother who first tells me about my grandmother's alcoholism. My father does it. He does it because he wants me to understand why my parents took Paula into their home.

She would have drunk herself to death, my father says. With her poorly leg.

I am 20 at that point, and my perception instantly shifts. My grandmother is not only a perpetrator, but also a victim. My parents are not only perpetrators, but in a way also victims of their own sense of responsibility.

My mother says she doesn't want to ask questions. 'I'm not asking' is one of my mother's favourite phrases. As though not wanting to know anything were a skill, an ability, a rule to be incorporated into the behavioural codex. But what she fears is not getting an answer. No matter from whom my mother doesn't get an answer, she feels hurt. So she has stopped asking. She was hurt too often when she did.

No one mentioned anything, and then I found a death notice in one of the photo boxes; by then, my grandmother was dead:

> *Hoping to see him again in the homeland, we received the still inconceivable news that our dear, good, hopeful eldest son, brother, brother-in-law and uncle, my dearly beloved fiancé Karl Scheffold (private in an engineering battalion) died a hero's death fulfilling his soldierly duty on 18 Nov. 1943, in the prime of life at 34. All those who knew him know what we have lost in him. We will console ourselves in the hope of seeing him again in our eternal homeland, and we ask you remember the dear fallen man in your prayers.*
> *Unterstadion, in the East, Karlsruhe, Bettighofen, Assmannshardt, Stuttgart, 15 December 1943.*
> *In deep and painful mourning, his fiancée Paula Haberbosch and all relatives.*
> *Memorial service at 10 a.m. on Thursday, 23 December, in Unterstadion, Ehingen district.*

My mother was not born until two and a half years later. She had no idea this man had ever been in her mother's life.

When I was born, my grandmother was 52. When I was one year old, my first brother died immediately after his birth. When I was two years and a few months old, my second brother was born prematurely, and no one could say whether he'd survive, and if he did survive, in what state. He survived as a happy child. My grandmother was the substitute mother of my childhood. She was there. But she was afraid. I know that because her fear draped itself over me like a veil: her diffuse fear of death, of strangers and strange men, of illnesses, of the Red Army Faction terrorists, burglars, traffic and planes, of storms and fire, of fertility and lust, of the forest and isolated areas and of all the other dangers my grandmother saw in life. I couldn't lift that veil for a very long time, and then when at times I could, it would always get heavier again whenever I saw my grandmother. To this day, the veil descends in my parents' house. When I am there, it's there too. Sometimes I also feel it elsewhere, trying to cover me again. It happens even though I have tried my hardest to get rid of it; it happens rarely now, though. My grandmother gave me the greatest sense of security and bequeathed me the greatest fear in my life. She was there when my father was away on business, she was there when my mother was busy with my brothers, and she was there when everyone had had more than enough of my nightmares. When I was small she had a room on our floor of a farmer's house surrounded by a big green field. The last room in the flat, at the very end of the corridor, facing west. It was small, with a sofa, a table, an armchair, a bed and a wardrobe. It got barely any sun but it had a view of the garden, the farmer's big barn, the clucking hens, the peace and quiet. When the fear came upon me, my grandmother told me there was no need to be afraid. Then she would let me lie next to her in her bed, which was 90 centimetres wide; the wall protected me on one side, and my grandmother's heavy body on the other. She would pray silently, the rosary moving in her hands like a snake, and I would fall asleep into her prayer.

When the fear came to her, no one protected me. The fear spilled over.

When I was 10, we moved into the house where nothing got better, and my grandmother got a flat of her own on the top floor. I became part of that flat, with my own room there. Between my parents' and my grandmother's flats was the stairwell, wooden steps linking the two floors and a cellar.

Memory does not follow a chronology; some things are very real, as if they were happening in that moment, very close. Some things come to me when I look at the pictures. If I want to think back to her life before me, I have to make up my grandmother, I have to enter her land of the dead backwards like the ancient Greeks did. But what do photographs tell us beyond the moment?

Sometimes, my grandmother takes the school bus home. She waits at the bus stop by the department store, laden with bags and shopping. She's on her way back from work. Schoolkids all around her, finished for the day; it's one o'clock. She's done an early shift or perhaps she had a doctor's appointment. She's been shopping. I know she's pleased when she can see me coming. I can almost see her heart leap; I see it in the crows around her eyes.

But on my face, two crevasses form between my brows. It happens even though I know there are things for us in her bags, things like chocolate and delicious pretzels. I try to pretend I haven't seen her. I try to run straight to Erich and the others so she won't see me. I see Erich and Stefan and I know my grandmother has already spotted me. I don't like it when I feel I ought to sit next to her, I don't like it when she sees who I'm talking to, and I don't like it when she wants to walk home with me from the bus stop. I'm only glad she's there when the fat man is on the bus, the one who always puts his hands between his legs as he looks at me and other girls. He gets off at my bus stop. Then I let her walk with me; then I let her protect me. She's not allowed to know that, though. We don't talk to each other because I never talk after school. She doesn't talk anyway. She only asks questions. She wants to know everything, but she never tells me anything.

On the bus, I sit down in the back row with the boys. Erika joins us, and a friend of Stefan's. The boys throw a backpack around. My grandmother is the last person to get on. I don't see her; I throw the bag at Erich and press it up against his back.

I know Oma won't ask who he is, because she knows him. She knows Stefan and Erika too. She'll ask who else was there, and I'll say I don't really know him.

I'm the first to get off. I know my grandmother will want me to carry her shopping, and I don't like to do that in front of the other kids. No one else I know gets off the bus. I pretend to be looking for something, so my grandmother won't see that I'm waiting because I think I have to wait. I spot an old apple on the ground, next to a garden fence. I manage to kick it out of its corner without touching anything else with my foot.

My grandmother is by my side now. Hello, I say.

So, she says.

I kick the apple along the road.

She says: Stop it. Come on, take a bag instead.

I fish the apple out of a drain cover and boot it like I could kick it all the way home. Then it's gone. I take one of my grandmother's two bags; it's very heavy.

Oof, I say.

She says nothing more.

As we're passing the town hall, she stops.

The wanted poster for the terrorists is up outside the town hall. I know she's afraid of them. Still, we walk past the display case especially and stop to look.

Mädle, she says, my little girl, they're dangerous.

I know that too, but I also know they won't harm me, so I say: They won't harm us.

They'll hurt everybody, she says.

Only politicians, I say.

I see her crossing herself quickly with her free hand.

I think of the man they abducted, Hanns Martin Schleyer, and the pictures on TV and the plane hijacking, and I remember suddenly that my father often flies abroad.

I turn away from my grandmother immediately. The thought that my father often goes on planes already scares me a lot, so I recite silent incantations: Dear God, please don't let anything happen to Dad. Dear God, please don't let anything happen to Dad. Dear God… I can't stop mumbling it to myself. I think I have to say it 10 times. Ten is a good number. Ten will be enough.

My grandmother is standing next to me in her dark blue suit, studying the wanted posters closely. In her black shoes, the joints of her big toes protrude visibly at the sides. She often goes to the chiropodist for them, two or three doors down from the town hall. I can't imagine my grandmother ever had nice feet. That's what I think as I look at the ground so as not to look into the terrorists' eyes; they're scaring me more than usual today. They always scare me but sometimes I like it. I don't dare admit that I know the wanted posters very well because I go terrorist-hunting almost every day. Sometimes Andrea comes with me. We roller skate outside the restaurant next to the town hall and jot down car number plates in a notebook. All number plates from other places are potentially dangerous, the owners of the cars potential terrorists. My grandmother mustn't ever know because she thinks exactly the same thing and then she'll be certain I'm in great danger every day. We walk across the town hall's forecourt, still silent.

Swine! says my grandmother.

I say nothing.

There are things that are directly connected to Paula, impossible to imagine without her living in our house. Most of them are to do with food, simple dishes that betray my grandmother's former poverty but taste good even though they're very plain. Bread dumplings for which she would collect stale crusts for weeks, brown plaited loaves, finger-shaped pasta she rolled by hand on a board, sweet steamed dumplings that we children loved, green parcels of vegetarian ravioli, sauerkraut, red cabbage, and so on. Dishes for which you don't need money. You need a cabbage, white or red, breadcrumbs or flour. You need a few eggs but there's never a shortage of chickens in a village. A garden with herbs. No meat. The only delicacy my grandmother would use was butter. My grandmother's cooking was almost effortless; it was as if it was her calling, her cause in life. In the kitchen, she was at peace with herself. Sometimes she'd talk to her dog, who was always with her in the kitchen. *Gang mer ausm Weg* – Get out my way; you'll get your treat soon enough; now you've had yours, she'd say. She liked the dog, but she kept even him at a distance.

I have stolen.

What did you steal?

I stole five marks from my grandmother – and two marks.

No more than that?

I did it a few times.

I'm sure you know the Ten Commandments well.

Yes.

Have you anything else to confess?

I insulted someone.

Who?

I told my mother she was a stupid cow.

And anything else?

I thought bad things about my grandmother.

We can kill in our thoughts, says the voice behind the elaborate wooden grille, louder now. I can tell that the priest, a man I know well, is shifting. I hear it. He knows my grandmother too. He knows her well, and he knows her sins, just as he knows mine.

I know, I say.

Then pray five Hail Marys and five Our Fathers as penance.

Yes, I say. Thank you, I say. Then I hear him praying for me.

I leave the confessional and sit down beneath the gallery in the large abbey church. I know I am lucky enough to pray in one of the most beautiful baroque churches in the country. It is an honour. It feels as though our sins are forgiven better here. Everything is magnificent. But I feel like crying. I have sinned and someone has to pray for me, and I have to pray for myself. I begin with the Hail Marys. Hail Mary full of grace, the Lord is with thee. Blessed are thou among women and blessed is the fruit of thy womb Jesus. Holy Mary Mother of God, pray for us sinners now and at the hour of our death. Amen.

I've thought a lot about the word 'blessed', because the farmer whose house we used to live in was always yelling: Blessed children! But you mustn't think about words like that when you're doing penance. You have to take the words as they come. Once I've said five Hail Marys I just know I didn't pray the first one well enough, and because I've only just confessed I have to say it again. I muddle my words, so I start again from the beginning. I have to pray it flawlessly and without false thoughts, otherwise the whole confession will have been in vain. Then I'll be in danger. After confession, you're pure. On the third attempt, I manage to say the whole Hail Mary with no thoughts or mistakes. The five Our Fathers take me a long time too. But I manage it. I'm very relieved and happy. For church, you wear a skirt or long trousers and a blouse; especially for confession. My grandmother was glad to see I'd put on my red blouse with the flower pattern.

The Lord God likes you like that, she said.

Next to the church, a path shaded by trees on either side leads down to the village. A green tunnel. It's a little bit spooky. It reminds me of the book *Where the Wild Things Are*. But on one side, here and there between the trees, I can see people walking along the cemetery path, and I know the dear Lord is looking after me again now that I have left all my sins behind, so nothing can happen to me.

I break a thick branch off a hazel bush. It's good for thrashing. I thrash leaves off the trees on either side of the path. I leave a trail. By the time I get home I feel guilty again about that.

My girl, says my grandmother. Now you're pure again. She strokes my head.

I'm 11 years old and I can already pray almost as well as her, that's what my grandmother says.

Aprons are her equivalent to jeans. My grandmother always wears one. The only exception is Sundays. Almost all her aprons have flowers on them. They are kept ironed and precisely folded in a pile in the cupboard. On top: little red flowers with white tendrils on a blue background. The next flowered apron: multicoloured blossoms intertwining, more of a dark green background. Next, red fabric with yellow and orange flowers, their tendrils wilder than on her other aprons. Then dark blue with pale blue and white. There are stripes between the braided flowers. The flowers are white. There's one khaki-coloured apron, edged in polka-dotted white piping, including around the pockets. Underneath that one, more flowers, blue ones, grouped in clusters or bunches. The apron pockets, the straps and the ties are plain. The flowers are dark purple with a red centre. Sometimes there's chocolate hidden between the aprons.

In my family it's important to look neat. Jeans are banned on Sundays, because Sundays are the day for light, friendly suits and brightly coloured dresses. Sundays are still the most dangerous day of the week, though. Bad thoughts constantly criss-cross good ones. Living in one house with my family is like being in prison. On Sundays, we go out for lunch to a nice restaurant. We're familiar with snails, frog's legs and even sea urchins. I'm a caviar kid. My father gets Christmas presents from Russia and other parts of the world. We love trying things other people find disgusting. We eat at least two courses. You're such a modern family, people say, but it only looks that way. We're a father, a mother, two children, a grandmother and a dog. The rabbit starts out living in our hobby room in the cellar, then moves to the garage. The budgie lives on the top floor, like Paula. I live there too. I don't want to live on the same floor as my parents because there's no space for me there. I'm scared of burglars in the cellar. I can't actually live anywhere in this house. Whenever possible, I escape to the garden, looking for places where I can pursue my thoughts undisturbed; I have to be alone to think properly. Usually, there isn't anywhere that's possible in the garden either, because all the places where I might be alone are instantly sought out by my grandmother. When I'm not doing the watching, I am watched. I am my grandmother's great mystery, although it's she who's the mystery. So I leave the house and garden on roller skates whenever I can. I practise like speed skaters, bending low, straightening my back, head forward and making wide arm movements until I hit my stride. When it's going well I put my arms behind my back, my hands locked, and stare along the road. Our road is about 300 metres long, one-way, and I skate along it at least 20 times in a row. I could go on much longer, I feel no exhaustion, all I feel is the thoughts in my head, no longer locked away. But eventually my grandmother always comes out of the garden and watches me. Pretending I don't see her, I head along the path down to the village. I pass the wanted posters by the town hall; I know the entire Red Army Faction on the posters by heart. I often stand here in my skates, looking at the dark photos, which sometimes follow me in my dreams. I know all the names to the photos and I've long since decided who looks scary and who doesn't. Susanne Albrecht looks nice, Inge Viett looks like a kindergarten teacher and I could imagine Sigrid Sternebeck being my cousin. I'm quite scared of Christian Klar, Adelheid Schulz and Brigitte Mohnhaupt because they look very dark and dangerous, and perhaps also because I've heard their names on the seven o'clock news. I'm 13 and I've read all the children's detective books. I know all about secrets and mysteries.

In deliberate silence, you lose track of the other people's voices. Your stomach makes noises and your heart makes noises and your head starts to hurt. You think you might have a terrible illness, you think you might die soon, and there's the fear. You sit in the deliberate silence and cannot say whether something is happening inside your body. You're sure it is. Your skin is peeling off your flesh, your flesh from your muscles, your muscles from your bones; you're unravelling, un-becoming. If someone doesn't say something soon you'll have to scream. And then the dog comes along and your hand strokes his fur, soft against your palms, and you know in a minute someone will say: We're at the table, no stroking the dog, and you move your hand over the brown dog's back, holding still while his cropped tail leaps to and fro, and there comes the voice to forbid it. You wipe your palm on your trousers and put both hands on the table and don't say anything in your defence. Knives scrape, sleeves brush, hands brush against the tablecloth,

47

no one says anything and then someone says thank you. Why not: You're welcome? Please talk to each other! It's the summer of 1979, the height of the Cold War, no sign of Gorbachev on the horizon. Not here at the table either. Through the open French window, blackbirds are singing. The neighbour starts mowing his lawn. Out on the road someone is riding a pedal car, you're certain.

When I listen to my grandmother these days, the times when her voice gets through to me, I fall into that other life, that other language, into a time that seems to have as little to do with my life now as the North Sea with the Indian Ocean. I hear her voice, which was quiet, gruff and unimaginable without the little lines at the corners of her mouth, which I can instantly see when I hear her speaking, just like that double chin she might not have had if she'd raised her head when she spoke. The voice speaks Swabian; it takes some effort to transpose into regular German and usually I don't want to. It's a rare enough occurrence that I hear her. When I do, I recognise a language in which I was never really at home even though I moved around in it, in which I never felt safe because I couldn't write it, because it differed from what I thought was beautiful when I read it, when I heard it. When I hear my grandmother's voice, we're sitting at the table and she says: *Du hosch doch so arg Hunger khet.* Which literally means: But you were so hungry. But really it means: Eat what's on your plate. When I hear her, she says: *Was duasch?* What are you doing? She's standing in the doorway to my bedroom, and I think that I never realised, as a child, that the many times when she stood in the doorway to my room were perhaps her moments of loneliness, the moments in which she heard *her* old ghosts, voices from somewhere, and prayer no longer helped. Moments in which only closeness helped. When her voice gets through to me, I fall silent. I sit at my desk, I look out at the chestnut trees that show the seasons just as well as fruit trees; I look at the huge church tower and think my grandmother wouldn't have liked the church because it's so big; I look at the square beneath the chestnut trees, the benches on which vagrants live in summer and warm up in the sun in winter. When there aren't any children playing down there, I hear Paula's voice as I write, falling softly into the silence into which she always fell. As though all her energy were used up after a single sentence. That one sentence was enough to put her hand back in her apron pocket for her prayer, which was possible without a sound, which needed only a hand on the rosary and the hope that it helped to believe in someone: Our Father.

I never heard her pray out loud. I only ever saw the prayers in her apron pocket.

I'm certain Paula never forgot the moment when Marie took her hand. Perhaps she took Marie's hand. Perhaps the photographer said, You're the prettiest girls in the village. I'm sure he said that because anyone can see that Paula and Marie were – at that moment, with their round girlish faces, clips in their hair and soft mouths. They were the prettiest girls as they stood there in the clearing with the photographer, the prettiest for miles around. In the eyes of the photographer, they were. Perhaps that was the moment when Marie took my grandmother's hand or my grandmother took hers, because they were certain everything in their lives would only get better. They were sure they could run off with their handleless bags under their arms (which we call clutches) or they wished they could. That was how they looked. It was 1932 or thereabouts and they certainly weren't thinking of war. When one war is just finished, another won't come along so soon, will it? No one thinks of war at 17, unless there's one going on. They had put on their winter coats because they were new; summer was over. It was that in-between time; the trees still bore their leaves but they had started changing colour.

It looks elegant, Marie said, when you don't wear a scarf with your winter coat, just a collar or a necklace. Marie was into fashion. Later, Paula was more into fashion and Marie was kitted out in modern looks by Gustl.

They've put on jewellery for the photographer. Perhaps we'll meet that handsome Karl along the way, Paula might have thought. I can only assume the handsome man in many of my grandmother's photographs was Karl. They were often photographed together. I'm sure Paula was never quite certain she was attractive enough for a man like him, because her beauty was inconsistent, even at 17. The man I believe is Karl, her fiancé, made her beautiful. Other photos tell a story of Paula's self-consciousness. There's that man sitting between the sisters and it's impossible to read from the picture to whom he belongs. Though Marie was a little too young, perhaps. In any case, it seems sometimes as if they were also never sure which one of them he meant, whether he meant her at all or whether he was seeing other girls like her. Perhaps the photographer told them to hold hands. Their father must have paid for these pictures that made his daughters even prettier than he saw when he looked at them. Photography has more weight than memory, more than reality. This is how it was, photography says. Though the trees still bore leaves, dead ones already rustled beneath their feet that day. In the girls' unlined two-dimensional faces, the sun glowed as if shining on a peaceful lake. Anything was possible.

Karl wore good, elegant suits, trousers tucked into socks that hugged his narrow feet softly, hand-stitched shoes. Perhaps he said they were English; perhaps they were English. He liked to wear bowties with his shirts. And his coats felt smooth and fine. That's what photography says. It's possible, though, that this man in the photos is not Karl at all, but a man who belonged to the family in some other way. Come dancing, Karl would say when he saw the sisters, and sometimes they would take a ride to the next village on his motorcycle. One after the other. Later, Paula may have thought: It could have turned out well, my life. It could have all gone differently. Perhaps she didn't want to think about it, perhaps that's why she stowed these photos in the very bottom drawer, so that they couldn't speak to her any more, so that they were no longer so easy to reach; she wasn't tempted to look at these photos and think, for instance, that that was the day when Karl kissed her. Perhaps Karl's death forbade remembering. No kissing dead men. But no, that day was the day with Marie. It was 200 metres from the village to the field where the photo was taken, and they walked back to the village. It was the harvest festival at church, that was why they were so pretty. And now she remembers: Karl really did join them and first he danced with Marie, then with her, and then with Marie again. Then a waltz with her. Everything was simple and good. Marie had soft hands, Paula thinks, and she knows that 'You have such soft hands' was one of Karl's phrases, and Paula had always been certain he said it to other girls and to Marie as well. Sometimes he would pull Marie onto the road and then waltz with her or whatever occurred to him. It looked like waltzing. Karl was different; when he was around, things had meaning. But that day, that had been the day of her and Marie, it was the day when they were the prettiest girls in the village. Everything was easy, even without Karl. That's not something we think often in life, about ourselves. But at 15, at 16, at 17. That's when we think that way. She thought that way once too, Paula thinks, now that she's daring to look at the photo. She can't do it without praying. She's got to the fifth decade. The rosary is a warm heart in her apron pocket. Even if she forgets everything else, she never forgets where she is in her prayer. The fifth joyful mystery: the finding of Jesus in the temple. Praying – for her it's as easy as breathing.

Or perhaps it was not like that at all.

Now that you're an adult, you still cannot understand that someone wouldn't ever voluntarily open their photo album and tell stories about their life. You certainly couldn't understand it as a child. That there are no stories, only the now, no memories of back then when your grandmother was a child, when she might have trusted animals more than people, like you. When it was her that talked to the animals because she was scared of speaking to people, like you. You cannot understand that someone can have no childhood, no love, no husband, no friends, no passion, nothing to move them. Nothing they feel is worth being told. The same deliberate silence setting in after most questions, the silence that made you get up and leave.

I'm watching my mother paint her fingernails. She has lovely long fingers and beautifully filed nails. She always paints them an elegant shade of red, sitting at the dining table.

I'm sitting at the table next to her, but far enough away not to disturb her. I tell her we've started practising table tennis on half the table, Ralf and I, because we've seen the table-tennis stars on television playing show matches on very small tables. I want to be able to do that too, I say.

My mother paints her nails.

I explain how Ralf and I keep moving further away from the table, how we practise our forehand topspin on half the table, how we hit the ball nonetheless. Then I hear my grandmother's footsteps on the stairs. I turn silent.

Not again, says my mother.

She's got as far as the first coat of red varnish over the base coat on the middle finger of her right hand. Usually, even her left hand doesn't tremble.

You're trembling, I say when I see it.

The door handle moves.

Can't a person even paint her nails in peace? says my mother, angry.

What are you doing? my grandmother asks.

You can see what, my mother answers.

And you? Oma Paula asks me.

I'm watching, I say.

Ich han bloss gucka wella, es isch so still gwesa, she says.

And that was probably true; she did just want to come and check on us because it was so quiet. But I only understand that now.

Shall I make some coffee? she asks.

Oma, you can see Mum's painting her nails.

53

She goes into the living room and looks out of the window. The bird house needs cleaning, she says.

I'll clean the bird house, she says. She looks at her daughter to see if she'll answer. But Mum looks only at her nails.

I sit perfectly still and look at no one. I hear my heart beating very loudly, because I can feel false threads being strung between the dining table, where I'm sitting with Mum, and the living room where Oma is – like electricity on the air. I think of the electric fence up the hill from our house, which is only ever charged when the shepherd has no time for his sheep. It's different here, though. Here, the electricity switches on when we might actually have time for one another.

Do you want to help me clean the bird house? my grandmother asks me.

I can't leave Mum here on her own, though, because then she'll think I like Oma more than her. I like cleaning the bird house with my grandmother a lot. I like the way the snow crunches beneath my feet. I like the way the seeds and bird feed stain the stamped-down snow underneath the little house. I know all the birds that visit the house: bullfinches, woodpeckers, blue tits, robin redbreasts, greenfinches and common sparrows. Sometimes a kingfisher drops in.

You like helping, my grandmother says, come on.

I don't move a muscle, look down at the table, not knowing what to do.

Have you had a row? she asks.

We were fine until a minute ago, my mother says. My heart thuds. I think it must be audible all the way in the living room, and I lean back in my chair because I don't want the table to start shaking. I wait for an answer from inside of me; I don't know what to do. My grandmother doesn't move.

Mum? I say.

You two do what you like, says my mother.

I leap up. I'm coming, I say.

I can feel that my grandmother is glad. It has grown uncomfortable next to my mother; for a moment I'm scared she's stopped breathing. She's staring at her hands, gives a quiet snort.

Shall I put on my fur boots? I ask. They're my favourite shoes right now.

Yes, says Oma.

Not for just three minutes, my mother says.

And a coat, Oma says.

It takes more than three minutes when we do it properly, I say.

My mother doesn't look up.

Perhaps it was like this: no one but him rode one like it. It was a Puch 500, Paula remembers that: VL, that was what Karl used to call the Puch, my VL, and her father used the word luxury, a new word in the village, a word that came out of nowhere all of a sudden and then it was there. When someone says luxury, Paula sees the Puch motorcycle and herself perched on it in a white dress. Parked outside the house, it looks like it doesn't belong. It was not just faster than the other motorcycles, it was better and better-looking too. And he was able to buy it. He didn't just take Paula for rides, he let Marie and the neighbourhood children sit on it too. You felt taller riding pillion. That was before Karl was called up, at least a year before, because they often took the motorcycle out to the mountains. That was when she first got to know the Swabian mountains and saw that there was more land there than people. Still, she wouldn't have wanted to live there. The first time the motorcycle roared up outside the house, Marie said: That's Karl. Because perhaps Marie saw through Karl better than Paula did. Marie ran out of the house, Paula rushed after her and their mother, no longer a good walker, came hobbling from behind the house where she was feeding the geese. Their father came down from the hayloft because the engine made so much noise. And when Karl stopped outside the house, their mother held her ears, and Paula already knew how the evening would go: her mother calling him a show-off who'd never come to anything if he went on like that and kept being such a spendthrift. Always has to have the best, her mother said. Her mother didn't mind much when Karl got called up soon after, but her father took it badly.

He let her climb onto the motorcycle first. Karl got off and helped her to get on; not that easy in a dress, but he was a gentleman. And her mother, she didn't say a thing. Her father did, because he was scared for her, but he also wanted his children to have it good in life.

He said: Look after my girl.

And Karl nodded and looked him in the eye.

When you've lost a son, you want your daughters to come to something. She hadn't done right by her father, Paula knew that. But he loved the little girl more than anything and the girl loved her grandfather back. He didn't take it out on the child that the villagers mocked the family. He took it out on his daughter though. He didn't speak to her, for weeks and months. When the first baby died, he didn't cry. Nobody cried. Who cries for a cripple? Even she was relieved. When the girl came, he asked: Whose is she?

And when she said nothing, he probably let it drop because he knew anyway. He wasn't stupid. And he made sure the girl never felt his anger.

Paula never told the story that way. But she never told it any other way either.

The bottle of Klosterfrau Melissengeist is always on hand, but unlike Rotbäckchen it's not fruit juice. It's medicine, my grandmother says. She says it's good for when you have a tummy ache, when your digestion's not working so well, when you have wind. It's not for children. It's for when your stomach's not well, when your tummy pinches. It's for sleeping better. It's medicine for everything. She says all that in her language, which I understand perfectly well but don't like speaking.

I don't really want to talk about her, my Auntie Marie said, or something like that, when my grandmother was still alive. I don't know anything much about her. Why do you want to know? You can see I have to force myself to say something. Listen, they were very different times. You couldn't just decide things. I was just lucky that things went better for me. No need to shake your head like that. No, that's not true, we don't have control of everything in our lives. Fate always had bad things in store for her. What do I mean by fate? I mean just that. She had a lot of bad luck. Bad things kept happening to her. No, fate isn't God. I know Paula says that, but I don't understand how. If God was fate, He wouldn't be a good God. So He's not fate. No, I'm not making it easy for myself. Yes, of course Paula believes in God, you can see that much. But she believes in a good God. Fate is not a good God. No, I wasn't there to see it. I wasn't there because I'd already moved into town by then. She was still back there even though she was the oldest sister. Yes, she was with the Werner family, no, the Webers, the Wengers – that's it: Weberer, that was their name, she ran their household for them. You know that already. But she was at Father's on the weekends. When our brother died in the war she got thrown off course; they were that close. And then, and then. I don't remember whether she had a fella. Believe it or not, I don't. Yes, it is possible not to remember that kind of thing. Don't believe me, then. No, she wasn't a beauty, but she was a merry one. Merry, fun, you know. She really used to be, once. As a child and then later as well, when she was your age. You have to remember the times; we didn't have a penny. I've told you already, I didn't know exactly what went on, I'd moved away. People talked. I don't know whether I asked. I think I never did. You don't just ask that kind of thing. Of course I'm her sister, but even as a sister you can't always talk freely. When you notice someone doesn't want to tell you something, you don't ask, you don't want to pry. Well of course I did ask, but I can't remember her saying anything. Yes, I'll try, I'll think about it again. Oh yes, it is possible. It's possible to know very little about your own sister. Oh yes.

Perhaps Auntie Marie could have told me the photographs' stories. I only knew a few of them while she was still alive. There was one album my grandmother didn't keep hidden. That was the album we were allowed to look at. But she wouldn't join us. It had photos missing. Why are they missing? I asked as a child.

Can't remember, my grandmother would say.

And who's this?

Frog doch it emmer so viel – don't always ask so many questions.

I'm watching her, like I always observe and jot down everything around me very closely. I'm hiding behind the freshly greened bushes, leaning against the neighbours' garage. I'm actually too old to be watching people. But I have to, to understand the house I live in, and my grandmother as well. I'm 13; I'll be 14 next month. Soon the plaster on the garage wall will leave bumpy imprints on my back. Ants crawl by. Birds fly up in shock at finding someone in their bush.

She's digging the garden. Her right ankle, as always, wrapped in a thick elastic bandage and hidden as well as possible beneath opaque stockings, she's standing on a wooden board. The sky is not quite blue; clouds scud above us like flags, and my grandmother rams the spade into the clayey earth with her right foot. Even if she puts all her not inconsiderable weight behind it, it takes one, two, three, even four attempts until the spade is in deep enough to lift a clump of soil. I hear my grandmother snorting with the effort. She wipes her face with her arm even as she's stabbing at the ground again, sways, loses her balance, stumbles and stands straight again; she thrusts deeper. My body jerks – it's impossible to watch my grandmother's movements without moving too. Perhaps she thinks the digging will get easier the more earth is turned over, but that's hardly the case; it hasn't rained for weeks. The soil is heavy with clay, and that's only fun in the rain. There won't be any potatoes planted in this garden anyway. My mother and my grandmother are at odds on the subject, as on so many matters, but at least they can agree on carrots. The children like them, they say. Everything's pinned on us. We like mashed potato too, though. When my grandmother stabs the spade into the earth, her skirt and her flowered apron ride up her knee, making the flowers sway in the spring wind, blurring yellow into red into green against the blue background. I know what kind of knickers my grandmother wears. I've seen her suspenders too. I don't talk about them; there's nothing nice to say. She keeps wiping her hand across her forehead but she's sweating so much it's no help. She brushes her hair back with her wrist and reaches for the spade, resting it against her hip more and more often. Strands of hair fall into her face; her bun has come loose. Now she slams the spade into the earth as though she'd been longing to do nothing for weeks but slam this spade into our garden, or in my father's garden to be precise, because he's the one who earns the money. As long as you're living under my roof – that goes for her, too. I know she can hardly spot any roots in the clayey earth, but she is certainly having an effect on the earthworm population, chopping them in two. She always does that. If I had been standing next to her I would have screamed. She always laughs when I do that, and slices the worms in half with the spade's sharp edge. It's good for the earth, she says. It's like the pleasure cats get out of chasing lizards. My grandmother knows no pity. Stab by stab. She announced over lunch that she's decided to dig over the garden up to the plum tree. The dog comes around the corner of the house and I almost call him, but that would put an end to my fun.

Alf trots down the length of the garden and stops where she is, wagging his cropped cocker-spaniel tail and looking like he's smiling.

Where have *you* come from? she says, as though Alf had gone missing, when she knows full well that the dog only gets out the house when one of us leaves too. She doesn't turn around. She knows who's coming to join her in the garden. There's something dangling off the spade, wriggling, and my grandmother jabs at the earth again, wanting it to stick to a clump of soil so that it's finally halved. She's not afraid of dead animals. She's afraid of thunderstorms. She's afraid of the woods because you always have a feeling you're not alone in there, because you can't see who or what is moving between the trees and bushes. Because the trees make the path through the woods narrow. She's afraid of men who might come around the corner. She's afraid for her granddaughter, me, more than for her grandson. You have to be more afraid for granddaughters. She's afraid when I spend half the day out on my roller skates. She's afraid something will happen while we're out in the car. She's afraid of the dark and of fishbones. She doesn't like fish. No one used to eat fish here in the village, she says. She's not afraid of fish but she doesn't like touching them. I love touching fish, stroking their scales one way and then back in the other direction to feel the tiny resistance; I like watching fish get scaled. My mother loves fish: steamed, fried, smoked. The dog gives a friendly whimper. He's still standing there looking up at my grandmother. She hears footsteps behind her, as do I. She knows who it is, she smells it and she doesn't like the smell, which is why she's gesturing like that. My mother still hasn't given up smoking. He hasn't either. 'He' is what my grandmother calls him. 'He' is my father. She simply goes on stabbing at the earth, lifts a clump, turns it, inspects the smooth surface left behind by the spade for a moment. It always looks good. Presumably, she doesn't hear herself groaning as she digs. She groans like crazy. She'll feel it by the evening.

My body's letting me know, she'll say then.

Most things in our house always happen the same way. Surprises are unusual.

You haven't got far yet, says my mother.

I know it's her the same way my grandmother knows it: she's sucking at her cigarette again. My grandmother hears her blowing out the smoke; she's close enough. She says nothing. The strand of hair falls over her face again and she brushes it away like before, then makes that same gesture again, fanning the air, which doesn't help at all.

How are you going to manage all this? my mother asks.

She shrugs.

There's so much left.

Plenty of time, says my grandmother.

My mother breathes out smoke. For a moment, the air loses its subtle scent of just-blossoming plum trees, of gorse, forsythias and grass. The dog trots back and forth along the garden path, not noticing me. They think I'm upstairs. The dog doesn't care where I am. My mother doesn't say anything more, just drags on her cigarette and goes back to the veranda, Alf close behind.

It's a hero's grave at which my grandmother is standing, before a wreath of white roses, wearing a long dark woollen coat, her folded hands in black gloves. Her head lowered, she is looking at nothing and I wonder who took this photo, who would photograph a woman at her fiancé's grave. Anyone who'd do such a thing, I think, has no respect for the intimacy of grief. But I don't know whether it's really immoral. I stare at the photograph like at a still life that conveys a certain story. Everything is obvious. The fiancé is dead. The would-be bride stands mourning at his grave. She is young and yet still old. She will have to find a new bridegroom, except – how often can you find a new bridegroom? My grandmother never found another. Or did she? Either way, there is no evidence of him, no grave, no message. Certainly not letters. My grandmother didn't keep any letters, or she never received any.

But perhaps there was once a kind of fiancé, before Karl Scheffold became one. Photos kept in a small folder suggest as much, enclosed as they are with the printed assurance that a 25-year-old man was given an orderly burial after falling victim to the war on 10 May 1940. Photos in which Nazis in uniforms are saluting death as if it were their king. Photos in which France, a pine forest, a village have become the setting for the burial of a man my grandmother must have known very well. Why else would she keep a separate folder with 20 pictures showing the coffin, the grave, the saluting soldiers, the troop leader holding a speech at the grave of a non-commissioned officer by the name of Ludwig Schwende, who was the exact same age as my grandmother; she never talked about either the burial or him.

Perhaps the man in the photos who I previously thought was Karl Scheffold is Ludwig Schwende.

The mourner I see in the photo at the hero's grave is 28 years old, but the woman I see is much older. I see an old woman. I see the same hardness in her stern face that she often wore, until her dying day; an impenetrable protective mask that allowed no tears to flow, even at her fiancé's grave.

My grandmother likes preserving.

Gselz. Plum gselz. Strawberry gselz. Raspberry gselz. Blackberry gselz. The jars are first boiled, then left on the draining board steaming hot; they have to be sterile. Plain gherkins go in pickling jars, the mustard kind too. For gselz, which is jam, my grandmother buys Mövenpick jam all year, which we have to eat up before she can fill the empty jars with her own gselz. At the end of the year, we still have jam from the previous year in our cellar, because we ate too many jars of Mövenpick jam. It goes on and on that way. Later, there are mixed pickles. Cauliflower and red peppers and onions and carrots. They go in pickling jars. My mother is in charge of those.

Many years on, long after my grandmother's death, my father and mother make relish and chutney together. My grandmother's Mövenpick jam jars are the perfect size.

I have pushed photos to and fro, sorted and arranged them anew. I have filled in the gaps along their white margins with writing. I wanted to give her, Paula, my grandmother, the life story she couldn't tell. It seemed possible. I ended up in an unknown place. It's like being nowhere. Too many of the experiences I shared with her seemed to clash with her earlier life, of which I knew nothing. That misled me into drawing conclusions from the life I do know to the one I don't. Fiction is always true, but not always truthful. I started again from the beginning. What I had to make sure I kept was the sense of truth, of disquiet.

Bartholomäberg. My grandmother only ever wants to visit pilgrimage sites and natural attractions. Sankt Bartholomäberg is both, which is why she likes it so much; the chapel is right there, reachable on foot every day, even with her poorly leg. Chapels are places of protection. She must have learned that that was not always the case, but she doesn't talk about it. The closer she can be to God, the better she feels. She's not afraid of the mountains, she's more afraid of the water, perhaps because her ancestors once came from there, at least that's the story. She doesn't say so. Her leg stops her from hiking into the mountains, but she doesn't mind. From up there, from the guesthouse where she always stays in late summer, there's a view of the valley, from behind the house up to the mountains, and she hears cowbells nearby and far off. The cows look healthier than at home. In the evenings, an owl hoots. She buys big bars of chocolate for me and my brother, and likes the way they call horseradish a different name to us, even though they speak the same language. *Kren*, it's called here in Austria. Once a year, we drive her and Auntie Marie and Gustl to their holiday guesthouse and eat at the best restaurant in town, because Uncle Gustl only ever wants to eat at the best restaurants. Uncle Gustl pays for anything we want from the menu. And now it's early morning and the floorboards creak as my grandmother steps out onto the balcony, the sun already risen and beginning to warm up the day. A nut tree casts a shadow across the path and the back garden. It is still quiet in the house; my grandmother likes that and at the same time doesn't like it. When it's too quiet, her fear comes, even though she knows there are other people in the building.

That's how I imagine it, that's how I see her in this place to which I often accompanied her, which I can still envisage clearly, the dark wooden building with its large balconies from which we looked far across the land, mountains upon mountains all around, and beds in which you sink so deep that nothing can happen to you.

She is 65, and age is leeching more and more into her already poorly leg, down to her ankle and into her foot, and it's in her stomach as well. Who knows how much longer she'll be able to travel. But up here, she can sometimes forget the pain; it's good for what ails her. Up here, it gets easier. I don't have to think of anything there, she says, and adds that she's not complaining, mustn't grumble.

That's how I imagine it when I think of her now, up there in Vorarlberg, where she was always slightly closer to heaven. The thoughts that so often rendered her absent come nonetheless, even more frequently in nice places. They come at night and by day, whenever it's quiet, but they don't come when she's praying. Prayer is a gift from God, my grandmother would sometimes say, once I had long since started seeing it as a burden. The thoughts also come when she's standing in the church to receive the Eucharist, and then they come as a guilty conscience. You're not worthy of opening your mouth and receiving this wondrous body. That's not true, she wants to say. It is true, she thinks. She has done nothing bad, she tells herself over and over. A balcony door creaks and she automatically turns her head, even though she knows full well who's coming out.

Guta Morga! You're up already, says Marie. Marie is wearing red velvet slippers, and when she comes onto the balcony Gustl is not far behind.

Where Marie is, Gustl is never far away. And vice versa. *De mei*, Gustl says when he means Marie, which means 'my wife', more or less.

He has the same slippers in grey. It's good that Marie has Gustl, although my grandmother didn't think much of him to begin with. It had always been the two of them, Marie and her. But Gustl is good for Marie. He's usually jolly, and it's easy enough to deal with his choleric moments. It's a problem he has, he talks about it sometimes.

What use is it digging up all this old stuff, Paula thinks.

Good morning, says Gustl. He's standing in the doorway, trousers on but no shirt over his vest. His sparse hair wet across his pate. His belly is as round as a ball.

He laughs. *Wo ganga mer heit nauf?* he asks.

Marie says: *Jetzt dua amol langsam.* She means he shouldn't be in such a rush to go hiking.

'S wird warm, Oma says, pointing down to the valley where the sun is already glistening off everything, making it shine. She's already standing slightly in the shade because it's too hot for her. Gustl and Marie sometimes still go up a mountain, but they also can no longer manage more than a hundred metres' height difference by now. Paula prefers to sit on the sun terrace in the village, under a shady roof. She has to put her poorly leg up, otherwise it swells.

Auf goht's, says Gustl.

Zieh d'r doch erst amol a Hemded a, says Marie – at least put a shirt on first. Perhaps Paula is sometimes a bit hard on Gustl because he's so fond of her daughter. My grandmother doesn't want to think that kind of thing, but the thought comes automatically. She goes back into her room. She's glad Marie and Gustl are here, but sometimes it's too

67

much for her. She goes to the wardrobe and takes out the blue cardigan; her daughter gave it to her. She likes the dresses and bags her daughter gives her, she likes them more than all the other things she has. Paula slides her slippers off. She can only put her other shoes on when she sits on the edge of the bed and jams her feet into her black Sunday shoes with a shoe horn. She hears herself groaning. What are you groaning at, she says to herself. Mustn't grumble; self-pity is not allowed.

The cardigan doesn't have a pocket so she has to take her handbag, otherwise she wouldn't know where to put her rosary. She hears Marie stalking around on the balcony.

Wo bisch? Marie calls out.

Paula doesn't answer. Marie knows perfectly well where she is and will soon barge into her room.

Was duasch no? asks my Auntie Marie, which really means something like: Get a move on.

I brauch no mei Dasch, says my grandmother.

Du brauchsch doch koi Dasch jetzt, says Auntie Marie. But the bag really is important to Paula.

Was woisch du – What do you know?

It's akin to a miracle when I can hear my grandmother so well.

I count 419 photos in my grandmother's boxes and albums. As though the sheer number of mute pictures might belie the lack of stories told about them.

It's an early afternoon in April, and my grandmother tips back her head and looks up at her flat. The blinds are closed. She often has them down because she feels unprotected otherwise. My grandmother doesn't feel secure in this house, I think, just like me. Instead of security and comfort, the house provides tension. Perhaps my grandmother and I feel safe and secure when I come to her bed at night after my nightmares. It gets warmer than usual in bed, too warm really, but another person's breathing makes it easier to fall asleep. To be precise, my grandmother's flat is a pretext. The room she once had in the midst of the family was perfectly good enough. But my parents wanted to build this house. For my grandmother, the change offers no improvement other than that she now has her own bathroom, which she only has to share with me. My grandmother spends hours sitting in her armchair, and if she weren't standing in the garden staring up at her window right now, she'd be sitting up there, the rosary snaking restlessly through her hand.

I've heard my grandmother saying we ought to have dug the garden in autumn, but because the frost came too early, the earth froze and then thawed, then came rain, then cold again, then snow, and this made the ground all the harder. And that my father ought to help out more and not do so much travelling. Brazil, Paris. My grandmother says the brochures from the Moulin Rouge are not suitable for children. She says I mustn't tell my mother she says so. She tells me that because she shouldn't really know about the brochures, I know that. They're in a drawer in my parents' bedroom. I've seen them too because my father showed them to us after a trip to Paris. My grandmother knows everything contained in the house, and she usually gets rid of everything that bothers her. She can't do that with the Moulin Rouge brochures, she knows that.

I see her come up against something very hard in the earth with the spade. She climbs onto the spade with her right foot but nothing gives way. I wonder what it can be. How does something like that suddenly get into the garden over the winter? I see my grandmother shrug. Then she reaches into her apron pocket again. It happens almost automatically, as it always does when she feels insecure. I make myself a little smaller in the bush, resting one lower leg on the ground because my foot is beginning to tremble. My grandmother wriggles the spade back and forth in the ground like a lever, but it doesn't look like anything comes loose. She pulls out the spade and thrusts it into the ground a foot further along; the spade stabs through. I see her pressing on the spade handle, trying to lift the clump of earth, but it seems to be very difficult. I realise my grandmother is running out of strength. I don't know whether to laugh or feel shocked. My grandmother has a lot of strength. I try to change position without rustling. My grandmother stands bent, then straightens up; she reaches into her pocket again. For a moment, she stands perfectly still, then she looks up at the sky. I count: one, two, three, four, up to 21. Then I look up too. Until I hear the sound of spade hitting earth again, the sound of its iron. And then I see my grandmother letting go of the spade and wobbling on the wooden board, and I jump up and out of my hiding place to run to her.

In a field there is a cow, and another and another. And one's standing, one's walking, one's looking, one's pissing, and one's shitting. Seeing that, you knew it had always been this way and would always be. And they all have different hairstyles and when they graze it sounds peaceful and calming. It's summer, and in the evening, when the cows are herded into their shed, it grows quiet.

They're tired. It's the time of bluebottles and horseflies. It's good when the nights grow cool. In the sky is the Plough and everything you need to imagine yourself in a different place. Stars, like islands. Up on the slope a fox skulks past, but no one can see it in the dark. In the morning, when the farmer's wife or the farmer's grown son or the old farmer start to move around the house, the cows start shifting too. They low, they make sounds, they speak. The farmer's wife comes for milking, the old farmer comes with feed. The farmer's son drives the tractor. The day comes into the cowshed, the milk flows into the trough, the truck pulls up to the house. It's still that way in some places. Except the milk had to be taken to the dairy by cart back then. You grew up where it was like that. And your grandmother's bedroom had a view of the farm and the henhouse and the vegetable patch, and there was a vastness that you now look for whenever you can. There was a vastness that your grandmother perhaps also looked for, later, when you moved into the new house. In that garden, you could hide like the fox; injured pigeons that landed there were nursed back to health; you could only be found when you wanted to be found.

I've turned 14. I've been given a record player and I've got my first record, Alan Parsons' *Eve*. I haven't got a clue about music because we only listen to random music in our house. Folk music, cheesy pop by Udo Jürgens, big-band tunes by James Last, Richard Strauss at New Year and sometimes on Sundays. Not a trace of Bach, nor of The Beatles or Pink Floyd. On Mondays, I watch *The Hit Parade* with Dieter Thomas Heck, sitting next to my grandmother. She hasn't got a clue about music.

My mother's not interested in it. Neither is my father. I bought the record after school. It was in a crate with other marked-down records. Perhaps it cost 9.99 marks. I was proud of the record because the cover looked good, two women in net veils looking young and attractive. Sexy. The record still looks good at home. And when I put it on the record player I'm surprised how much I like it. I listen to it over and over; I can't stop listening to the track 'Lucifer'. I forget everything while I'm in my room listening to 'Lucifer', but my grandmother doesn't like me forgetting everything, and it's as if she can't tolerate a piece of music under her roof that's as exciting as that title. I listen to music with the door closed; I've begun allowing myself to close my bedroom door. I've stopped leaving the door ajar. My grandmother doesn't like that. When I close the door and 'Lucifer' sets in, my grandmother appears in my room. She doesn't say a word. She watches me like an animal in a zoo, when all I'm doing is sitting on the orange carpet, leaning against the bed and listening to music. I try not to take any notice of her but she doesn't leave.

Can't you turn it down?

I don't want to turn it down.

She goes over to the record player. I don't think she's ever operated a record player in her life. I'm afraid for my one record, and I leap up.

That's my record, I say. This is my room. She stands still for a moment. I leap up and position myself in front of the record player.

Turn it down, she says.

Scared that she'll do it herself, I raise the pickup arm.

She turns around and goes out, leaving the door ajar.

I close the door. I lower the needle back onto the blank groove before 'Lucifer'. Crackling. When the song sets in I forget the crackle. I listen to the whole song. I feel good. Once I've relaxed again, I move the needle back to the beginning and lie down on the bed under the dormer window and look up at the sky. I'm so happy to be lying there with the clouds floating by above me that I close my eyes, and suddenly I'm so far away that I don't notice the rustling until it's close at hand. It's my grandmother's stockings, rubbing against each other between her hefty thighs.

What are you doing? she asks, and I can't see the sky any more. Her skin hangs loose; when she leans her head forwards, she has a double chin.

I feel like I've been caught enjoying something I shouldn't have. It's as though I'd been touching myself and my grandmother saw me. I'm ashamed and I stammer something, shocked. I hate myself at that moment. I don't shout. I don't say: Get out of here. Nor do I say that I don't dare touch myself because I'm scared she'll catch me in the act. I don't say I'm scared to touch my own body. I don't say: Out of my room! Nor: Why are you watching me? I get up, turn off the music and leave the room, which is my room, which she's taken possession of. Again. I go downstairs and tell my mother I can't live up there any more.

My mother says she understands me. But where else could I live?

My brother lives downstairs. And there's no other room, apart from the master bedroom and the living room, which is an open-plan space with the dining room and the hallway.

I live in a house with no space for me.

Later, I'll say: My grandmother can't distinguish between herself and me, her granddaughter.

But I am allowed to listen to music in my room. Of course, says my mother. Just close the door.

I say that I do close the door, that I listen to music quite loud but not too loud.

I know, my mother says.

I don't want her just coming in without knocking.

Tell her that, my mother says.

I have told her.

Help me, I say, but I know my mother avoids any conflict with my grandmother; she's scared of her own anger. My mother's whole life is a conflict with her mother. That's why she constantly has to avoid her. They walk around in the same house, and as soon as my grandmother approaches my mother, she tries to run away.

My mother is sitting on the sofa. The cocker spaniel is wagging around us like he's happy, or perhaps because he wants us to be happy. My mother hasn't put her magazine down. She flicks through it. I watch her and say I could maybe move into the basement. I get up. I go down to the cellar and look at everything. There's the middle cellar room where we dry the laundry. It has a light shaft as a window so it's pitch-dark in there. I go into our hobby room; that's where the table-tennis table is. If I cleared away the table it would be a big room. It leads out to the garden; there's a door and a window to the outside. Everyone passes them when they go to the outdoor stairs. I stand there and know that fear would only follow me down here, fear of the footsteps outside, fear of someone seeing that I live all on my own in the basement and attacking me. I realise the cellar is not the answer.

My mother's standing on the veranda now, smoking a cigarette. It's cold. But at least she hasn't got a magazine with her. The dog wags around her legs.

I can't live in the cellar either, I say. My mother shakes her head.

Why don't you say something to her?

She exhales smoke. Angry, she says: You know there's no point. She went through my bedside drawer when I took the dog for his walk this morning.

How do you know?

I just know, she says.

My grandmother works as a cleaning lady in a big pharmaceutical company, so there are some days when she's not at home. They are good days because my mother is relaxed. Sometimes they're even very good days. We talk to each other more. My grandmother doesn't tell us much about her work. Nothing much to say, she says. The most important thing is that she gets out of the house, sees other people whose names she never mentions, goes to a job where you have to pass through airlocks in protective clothing, where you're deliberately silent because you're too caught up in the protective clothes and your own thoughts.

For many years, I thought my grandmother had been raped. Why else would someone maintain such stubborn silence about the father of her own child, about her own life, unless she was traumatised. Then my mother received a phone call that proved all that wrong: Your father's in our hospital. And my mother put the phone down because that couldn't be, because it was inconceivable to her just then.

So there is a father, who knows about his child.

When my great-grandparents' grave is cleared for re-use, the cemetery also clears the place where my mother's older brother, the child with the split back, was laid to rest. I'm now convinced there is a father for that child, too, a man who isn't a rapist. I will never be entirely certain, though.

I find a pair of white gloves. They're too big for my slim hands but I think they're gorgeous. The gloves are inside a small cardboard box, and the box is suddenly in my wardrobe. There's a lucky charm in there, a wooden ladybird, old and yellowed, and a few of the cards with holy pictures given to people for communion, which my grandmother always puts everywhere when she wants to fend off fate. She has a lot of them. I don't know where she gets them from. Perhaps they sell them on the coach during the pilgrimages my grandmother regularly makes. One of the pictures is of a child cradling a sheep, his cloak a beautiful shade of orange. The boy is wearing a cross. I like the pictures but they do scare me as well. They always mean something. I'm in danger. Why has my grandmother put this box in my wardrobe?

The gloves are so silky smooth that I never want to take them off, but because the holy pictures are in with them, they suddenly seem dangerous to me. They're flawless; they don't belong to me. But they were in my wardrobe. What happened to her with these gloves that my grandmother has to move them to my wardrobe, what does she want to invoke? Why can't they stay in her wardrobe?

I feel myself getting angry. I take the gloves off, put them back in the box and then I go over to my grandmother's room.

What's this all about? I ask. Why did you put these gloves in my wardrobe?

She looks up only for a moment, then back down at her lap.

I see the right hand in her apron pocket turning into a creature. I think of weasels, or ferrets, like my friend Christian has at home. I think of that place for a moment, that nice house, his warm-hearted mother, his generous father. I think of how they talk to each other at mealtimes and how comfortable I feel with them. I'm ashamed of these thoughts. I see my grandmother staring into space and I see her hand praying. It's as though she's masturbating with the rosary, I think, and at the same moment I think that I mustn't say anything now. If I say something wrong I'll be punished. *Our Father, who art in heaven, hallowed be Thy name*, I think, and the words recite themselves inside me. I can't help it, it's like a compulsion. It's my salvation. I see my grandmother's hand moving faster and faster, my grandmother praying a turbo-Our Father, and that new speed lodges unspoken in my mind. I stand next to my silent grandmother and speak one silent turbo-Our Father after another. The budgie hops around in its cage, excited. Bobby, shhh, says my grandmother. She looks up at the bird for a brief moment and the bird stops for an equally brief instant. Then it returns to dangling by its beak from the bars of its cage; and it is as if the movements of my grandmother's hand in her apron pocket and the hopping of the bird behind the bars and the prayer in my head merge and cast a spell on me.

I'm standing in her room clutching the box of gloves, and I can't move, *for Thine is the kingdom, the power and the*

77

glory, for ever and ever. Amen. I put the box down on the table in front of my grandmother. I leave the room.

I write a story for the white gloves, because every object has a story and these gloves must have a special story, otherwise my grandmother wouldn't have kept them, wouldn't have wanted them so far away from her and at the same time so close to me.

He gave her a pair of white gloves. Covering her like a swan's plumage, they came halfway up her forearm. Look, he said, and gave Paula a rustling pink package.

She felt the tissue paper in her hand and saw the sticker, and even if she hadn't seen it, packages like that only came from the expensive shops in town. She'd never been to most of them. What you don't know, you don't miss. The package was light and felt soft. She saw him looking at her, pleased that she was so shy. Perhaps also pleased because he saw how much it muddled her, all of it. All she could think of was how the place around them looked; and that the package didn't quite fit into the surroundings, she felt that too.

You look beautiful, he said.

But if she looked so beautiful, she didn't fit into this house, not any more. How could you look beautiful and live in a house in which nothing was beautiful? That was why Paula couldn't open the package.

He took her hand and said: Go on, open it.

She had to shake her head. I will, later.

He didn't understand that.

They went to their field. His hand on the small of her back. In her hand, the package. She can't remember what they talked about. He had more money, he was far cleverer than her, he could talk. He'd been to Munich once. He was superior to her in every way.

She had three dresses, three camis, one pair of good shoes, one coat for summer, one for winter. There was nothing else she could let him see. She'd been to Lindau once. Perhaps it had to turn out the way it turned out, because they weren't at all suited, not really. If it hadn't been the war that separated them, it would have been something else. Back then, she wouldn't have thought that. The Lord knows best: that's what she thinks now.

In the meadow, they sat down side by side. Open it, he said.

She still remembers how good he smelled. And she thinks if she'd ever smelled him again, later on, all her feelings would have returned. She's not sure whether it was good or bad that that never happened. Perhaps it was a good thing.

When she unwrapped the package she instantly thought of swans, and that her hands were far too rough for them. That was her first thought.

Put them on, he said, and then she knew he had bought the gloves to go with her white summer dress with the red flowers and the puff sleeves, which she was wearing right then. It was the dress she always wore to meet him. It was the only elegant dress she had.

They match your dress, he said.

She was surprised he knew how large her hands were, had picked out the right size. You look like a lady now, he said.

She did feel beautiful, but also a little bit of an imposter. Always did, as if she didn't deserve it. He's wrong, she thought. She'd been jealous of Marie, with whom he was jolly and spoke much more freely. Really, he wanted Marie, but she was just too young. One day he'll have Marie, she thought.

They had both looked at her hands, he resting on one elbow on the grass. She sitting next to him. Her white swan hands.

When should she wear these gloves?

Always.

To this day, she thinks Karl really wanted Marie. To this day, she believes in this delusion, which only one person could clear up. Him up there. And He did. If Karl had come home from the war he would have wanted Marie, because she'd got even more beautiful in the meantime. And then it would have been over between her and her younger sister. She could never have stood to see Karl kissing Marie. Marie could say as often as she liked: You're wrong, he only has eyes for you. She doesn't know what's true. She thinks she loved Karl. But can you love someone who doesn't suit you? For a long time, Paula doesn't know where those false white hands went. She never saw them after that.

And suddenly they turned up again, and with them the whole story.

But perhaps it was all very different, and it was Ludwig Schwende who gave her the gloves. And it might just as well have been neither of them, because there was another man.

There is a house and there's a garden behind the house and the garden is also a goose meadow and there's the dog. There's the woman in the kitchen who's drunk at noon and at night. There's the woman in the kitchen who sends her daughter next door to do the cleaning, the sad drunk woman in the kitchen who doesn't hit out with her hands, but by not speaking. There is silence that is deliberate and loud. There are shelves of preserves, there is wood in the corner, there's a stove to be fired. There are potatoes. There's the sack of flour and the flour scoop. There are onions in the garden and the leathery apple tree and the gnarled pear tree; there's rarely meat on the table. There is the daughter's grandfather, and his presence seems to say that someone has taken pity on her after all. There are the mean words that hit the daughter but are aimed at the mother: bastard and Polack and gypsy. They tally up the world that's unknown in the village. Someone wants to know, but no one knows anything. Who can you ask? There is no language for nothingness. There is the silence. There's the fur of the rabbits in the hutch and the chatter of the geese outside in the garden, on the way to freedom. There is the little black dog by the girl's side, the spitz; there are the animals that snuffle and bark and gaggle, and they offer their fur and their feathers to the girl's hands. There's a very pretty girl. She doesn't look like she's from these parts, she doesn't have eyes from these parts, and she doesn't have the build of the girls in the village. She's slim and tough and wiry, and when she speaks she takes life seriously. There are pigeons in the hayloft; if only you could give them a letter for a man you don't know! And if only they'd fly off with the letter and if only they'd arrive. If only he knew she existed! the girl thinks. But they're not carrier pigeons, her grandfather says. They're our pigeons, sweetie, and you've got me. If only that were enough. But what if the man who's *not* here was the best man in the world. That could be true. That's something the girl can imagine.

That's about what my mother told me, later.

There's the herd of geese behind the house, and around the herd of geese there's a fence. The fence is too high for the girl but the geese clamour, and the girl understands that the geese want to get out of the fence, she knows they do. And because the girl is not very tall and not very strong, she grabs the geese one by one by their long necks and heaves them over the fence. That doesn't go well, it's a disaster if ever there was one, involuntary murder. Nothing helps, not even praying. Her grandfather rages and her mother calls her a waste of space. She knows that anyway, even though she does the neighbour's cleaning for her mother. Even though she's only 12 or 13. She knows how to clean. And how death comes, she knows that now too. And what loneliness feels like, once she doesn't have the dog any more. Then there's the house and a bed in a room she doesn't like, and there's the grandfather, until he's not there any longer either, and then there's nothing left. Only the mother, drunk and later with a poorly leg.

I've had a recurring nightmare ever since my childhood. It pops up with every new place I arrive at, with every new man who comes into my life. I'm in a strange toilet cubicle and suddenly I realise someone is climbing up the outside of the cubicle, and I already know that this person, a man, will manage to get in and get me. Get into me. And I scream but I have no voice. Later in the dream, my voice returns and wakes me up, or the person sleeping next to me. I've been having the dream since I was 10 years old. It first came when we moved out of the farmer's house, which

I loved, into our own house, which I never learned to love. I don't know how or why the dream first came to me back then; all I know is my mother and grandmother's terrible fear that something might happen to them in strange places, in the woods, somewhere they don't know their way around. For a long time, that was my fear too. After a lot of travelling, some of it alone, after a lot of changes in my life, the fear subsided. But that toilet nightmare has stayed with me.

The first thing I do is check whether anything is written on the back of the photographs in my grandmother's boxes, but usually there's nothing but a number.

A924 is the most beautiful picture I find among the photos. It tells of a luscious, good, beautiful life, or at least of a day like that out in a meadow beneath blossoming fruit trees, of laughing people eating and drinking and looking calm and elegant in their carefree way. I don't recognise anyone in the photograph. I see three women, two men and two girls sitting underneath a tree. Another girl is standing behind the small picnic group, looking at the camera, cheerful and confident. It's a photo that must have been taken before the Second World War, or perhaps just at the beginning. I can tell by the car's bodywork; cars looked different later on. The car in the background is a Mercedes, shiny and cared-for or even new, a family vehicle of the kind only driven in well-off circles, an expensive dark limousine. My grandmother was a housekeeper for a family like that as a young woman, and as a not quite so young woman, so perhaps the picture was a gift to her from another life, a thank-you or a souvenir of a good time, of summer days in white dresses and white shirts with striped ties, with scarves slung around heads, elegantly knotted, berets and children in sundresses and white stockings, not afraid of life. Not a bit.

Holding the photograph like I have so many times before, I notice through the magnifying glass the dress worn by the young woman nestling up to the clearly older woman and leaning against a tree, and I look more closely. I'm sure I know that dress. I look for proof, going through my photographs again until I have it: it's the dress my grandmother is wearing in the gloves photo. And that's how I find my grandmother sitting on the grass in that dress and smiling at the photographer with the most infatuated eyes I can imagine. And when I use the magnifying glass again I see the gold watch later kept in a case in her chest of drawers. My grandmother is perhaps 20 in the photograph. *Foto Franz, Biberach/R.*, is stamped on the back.

I know she wants to go to church. Before church she takes her apron off in the hall, takes her everyday skirt off in the bathroom, and slips into the tight skirt in which she can only take small steps, her tights rustling. It doesn't sound exciting. Her tights are skintone. I hear it through the closed door, and what I don't hear, I know. Underneath the tights she wears huge white knickers, almost down to her knees, which are fat. I hear her walking up and down the hall, I don't want to hear it but it's impossible not to. I feel threatened by her presence outside my door. I can no longer think or read. I can listen to music, but only if I turn it up loud. I'm listening to Simon & Garfunkel; my record player crackles a bit but that doesn't matter because the crackling and the music form a new space, a space just for me, a hiding place made of unfamiliar voices, crackling and sounds. It shuts my grandmother out. But not for long. She doesn't knock, she's suddenly simply in my room. She's wearing a suit that fits her perfectly and suits her well, she's carrying her black handbag, she smells of hairspray. She's dressed up for the Lord. She says she's going to church now. I nod. It's good when she goes to church, because then I can turn my music off, open the dormer window and listen to the birds. Go on then, get out of here, I want to say. But I can't. She gives me a piercing look. She looks at me as though even my sitting on the bed were a mystery and as though an even bigger mystery were hidden under the bed. I am a mystery. But all I am is 14 years old and wanting my own space.

I'm going now, she says, and when I don't respond she doesn't leave. She stands in the doorway, not stepping any closer and not leaving the room.

I say: Why are there suddenly three of your dresses in my wardrobe?

She doesn't even shrug.

I'll be back later, she says.

And it sounds to me like a threat.

Tell her to take her dresses out of my wardrobe, I say to my mother. She only does it so she has an excuse to go through my things, I say.

I get no protection. I know my mother is glad my grandmother's curiosity is not only focused on her; it's better distributed when my grandmother keeps tabs on me as well as her. My mother won't say anything to her.

I don't want my grandmother to touch me any more. I can't even hold out my hand to her without effort, fear-ing she might never let it go. She clings to me, eating me up like the wolf did Red Riding Hood. She'll make me turn into her, she'll make sure there's no difference left between her fear and mine, between her prayers and mine, between her worry that I might be seeing men and mine that I might get pregnant from a boy without sleeping with him. Just from kissing, just from going out with a boy. I don't want anything more to do with my grandmother. And yet I often need her, badly. When the fear gives me stomach cramps at night, when I get nightmares in which my hands grow huge and turn into monstrous foreign bodies. But I want nothing more to do with her.

They're facing each other at the table. My mother and my grandmother. That's the rule whenever my father is out of the house. That means they've sat facing each other over coffee every afternoon since my grandmother gave up working. I don't know why they drink coffee together. They don't like sitting at one table. But they do it. Every afternoon. I get called down for coffee as well and I sit in the place next to my mother. That's my place. Always. There are sweet pastries, nut swirls and doughnuts. There's shrapnel. Shrapnel is a calorific bomb with an even more martial name, which no one seems ever to have thought about: a peaked hill of nougat surrounded by lots of chocolate. For a while, it's my favourite sweet. One day, there's a sweet pretzel made of a kind of flaky pastry, something new; the two of them share it.

My mother takes one half and my grandmother the other.

Very nice, she says.

My mother says nothing. She chews, takes a sip of coffee, and then she asks: Have you done your English?

I nod.

Enough?

My grandmother says: All she does is listen to music.

I say: Yes, English music.

My mother says: But you won't learn anything.

You can learn more than you think.

I can see it coming, she'll get another D, my grandmother says.

How do you know? I ask.

If not worse, my grandmother says.

How do you know I got a D?

I saw it, my grandmother says.

Where? I ask. I make sure I take my school bag downstairs straight after finishing my homework, and I put it with the other bags in the hall because I don't want my grandmother to riffle through it. It's true that I got a D minus. I'll get better marks from now on because I listen to English music, I know I will.

No one says another word at the table until my mother says the plants need watering this evening.

My grandmother says she only just watered them yesterday.

I get up, take my plate and cup and put them down next to the dishwasher in the kitchen.

Back up in my room, I turn on the record player. I translate song lyrics into German. I cry when I listen to 'The Boxer'. I don't know if it's the lyrics or the music or just because I feel like crying.

Once again, I don't notice my grandmother coming into my room.

She doesn't say a word, just watches.

I don't look at her. I sit hunched over my pad, tears smudging the ink. I don't want my grandmother to see.

She stands next to me and looks down at me and my writing pad. I pick up my ink-eraser pen and run it over the smudged letters. *I kill you*, I say quietly in English. I'm shocked at myself. I hear her breathing, feel her staring at my head. Out of the corner of my eye, I see her hand moving to her apron pocket. Then my grandmother leaves again, not closing the door behind her. I pray. I pray until I'm certain she won't die from my words. Ten Our Fathers, five Hail Marys, flawless.

Now each of us is both, my grandmother and I: watcher and watched.

To protect me from my grandmother's eyes and ears, from her control and her dear Lord who sees all, I watch her as though something might happen to me at any moment, through her. I watch her in her absence, as though she's already present again, I watch in anticipation by controlling myself precisely, I choose what I'll say when she's there and what I won't say, what I'll leave in my room and what I'll hide, and what I'll wear so as not to arouse her suspicion. I develop strategies to satisfy her and her curiosity; I lay bait to set myself free. It rarely works. My grandmother gets into every nook and cranny of my life, as though it's where she experiences hers.

This is what my mother remembers.

They were under the bed and behind the kitchen bench and in the wardrobe and the house smelled. The place smelled like her mother smelled. And it smelled when you unscrewed the lid from the bottle, yet it looked as clear as water. And it smelled acerbic and it was liquid, which my mother hated even as a child and later too, and if it was brown she hated it even more. It was brandy. And the brandy was never empty, there was brandy like in a sacred fount, brandy like the porridge in the fairy tale that flowed and flowed, even when money was tight. There was brandy all over the house; it mostly smelled of plums. It had to stop, her grandfather said so too, and the girl who was my mother knew her mother wouldn't stop. Not just like that. Why stop? What else could you do when you were bringing up a Polack's child, when seeing the bastard child permanently reminded you that things should've been different? You drink brandy and then you don't see as straight, or you see things differently. But really the girl didn't care why her mother drank, it told the girl nothing because it only meant her mother wouldn't respond and would slur her words and send her to do the neighbour's cleaning so she could buy more brandy, as much as she needed. And later, later she knew that if she left her mother behind in her old house with her plum brandy, it would be the end of her. And with her poorly leg. Then it would be the end of her for ever. And she remembers it was only warm where the animals were and her grandfather and the dog, who was a very special dog, a dog who was always by her side, who made all the bad things better. She remembers the day when the dog died, remembers very clearly how suddenly there was nothing left that was good. How the smell of brandy got bigger and bigger, because there was no more smell of dog. How her grandfather wanted to console her and couldn't, and how everything repeated itself when her grandfather died. How emotionless that left her mother. How it was when no one spoke to her any more, no one laughed with her.

She had to stay. Because there was a secret. The secret harboured happiness and joy and the promise that everything might be better – if only it was revealed. If the man whose name she didn't even know were to be granted a name, a voice. If a person were to come out of nothing. Her father. That's why she had to stay, and she stayed. And that's why she couldn't leave her mother alone with her brandy in her house. There was no other reason.

Outside, the full moon rises above the mountains, its light revealing the bodies of the animals grazing and resting, the cows. The fox crossing the road from field to field, the moon's shimmer stroking its fur. And the cows looking up at the light in the sky, their silhouettes turned towards the big pale ball. The cattle's stillness as the landscape brightens beneath the moon, and you understand once again that stillness and deliberate silence are different. And you long to bathe in that light, in that soundless beauty, in that feeling of being capable of living without language; as the animals demonstrate by halting or confidently moving. They barely make a sound, but when they do it's a good sound. How markedly different it is when sounds break through deliberate silence, how threatening a cleared human throat sounds out of silence, or into it.

We don't talk about the fact that I regularly relieve her of one, two and five-mark coins. If we did talk about it, she'd have to admit that she takes away my magazines and tracks down my diary, no matter where I hide it. I'd say to her: That's exactly what you're paying for, and for reading my letters, the notes I exchange under the desk with Jörn or some other boy at school; for removing my blood-stained sheets, which are no more your business than my trouser pockets and my wardrobe.

My grandmother and I don't have an arrangement; everything arranges itself.

Is it really that important to know where you come from? I don't care, my mother says, later. Her refusal when someone called her from a hospital: Your father is a patient here and wants to speak to you one last time.

No, that can't be true, my mother said, and she hung up. She couldn't imagine someone would turn up out of the blue after 45 years and say: I do exist. Or perhaps it was because she didn't want to imagine it any more. And to this day, I wonder what happened to her hope that there might be someone like her, or someone better than her mother. The better person. Or did she say it because she was afraid to face reality? Why that determined 'No, that can't be true'? But perhaps deprivation had simply devoured all hope. Today, she says there was something not quite clear on the telephone, something that made her certain it couldn't be true.

It was 1992 when it happened. A receiver put down could not be picked up again. Telephones were still contraptions with dials, and you couldn't see who was calling, and hung up was hung up. She didn't tell anyone until weeks later.

My mother says it's not so bad because she's finished with it. I haven't finished with it because the questions never end: Where does our hair come from, our eyes, our stature, my mother's and later mine? My mother's fear of finding out something terrible, of 'gypsies' who want to read her palm; she thinks he will be there in her hand, her father. Or she thinks they want to do it because her father was one of them. One of those 'gypsies'. And the way she pulls back from everything unfamiliar and different and yet never stops praising it. Even defends the right to be different. And her giving me a black doll. The doll is a boy and I call him Bobby, like my best sandpit friend. In my imagination, the two Bobbies are twins, and I love the doll because he's different and at the same time a child like me.

Paula can't be an old woman, at this point she can't even be middle-aged. And yet she is the haggard old woman in the photograph next to the tall young woman with the crooked but long legs, holding a small child and wearing an apron, which my grandmother is not, for a change. I don't know the other woman. I have no idea who the boy with the very neat haircut is, wearing pleated trousers and a shirt, and beaming like he's on a spot-lit stage right next to the greatest idol of the day.

The old woman is smiling too, the one who can't be an old woman and is plucking at her neat white blouse, tucked into a long dark pleated skirt. Yet even though she wears that joy on her withered face she looks bad, as bad as all alcoholics look when alcohol has become the focal point of their lives, when there's nothing left but the desperate happiness of being able to drink. And I see the white streak in her tied-back hair, that streak I have inherited from my grandmother, which grew in at the age of 20 and rested beneath my black hair like a white wave.

When I find another photo from the same series, I realise they're pictures from my mother's First Communion. My grandmother is about 40 in them. In her white communion dress, my mother looks like a princess from a faraway kingdom.

By the time I'm born and old enough to be interested in people and their teeth, my grandmother already has false teeth. The drinking put paid to her real ones. Now she's not a drinker any more. Sometimes she takes a sip of Klosterfrau Melissengeist and sometimes, later, she'll have a glass of beer with a meal. I can't remember ever seeing her drunk. In the photographs of her holding me as a baby, she looks plump and good and healthy. My parents saved her from herself.

Your mother has her troubles, says Auntie Marie, but she doesn't talk about them. She's a tough one. She was as a child, even. When they all called her those terrible names.

What names?

I can't say them these days, says Auntie Marie.

What did Oma do that's so bad she can't tell us?

Paula didn't do anything bad, Marie says right away. And if she had, I wouldn't know about it. I certainly don't know anything bad. Well, later, when she started drinking. But she never harmed a fly. I can tell you that.

She used to send Mum to that man to do the cleaning.

He never hurt her. He was on his own, that's all. Didn't have anyone, he was bitter about life. A sourpuss. Nothing more than that. But she didn't have to go for that long.

93

She didn't even let her keep the money.

Who do you think had money for themselves back then? What would she have needed it for? There wasn't anything to buy in the village.

Things children want: sherbet or lollies.

Your grandmother was so poor there was no money for that kind of thing.

But my mother did the cleaning and Oma spent all the money on drink.

That's a different matter. She was unhappy. You can't imagine – for a while, Paula was the unhappiest a person could be.

And then?

Then she was still unhappy. And then came her foot.

Leg.

Her poorly foot, you know that, so she can't walk properly.

It was better when she still went to work.

Because she got out and saw people. Even if she doesn't talk much.

People knew her in town. At work. And now.

You know how it is now. She goes to her pensioners' afternoon. That's the right thing to do when you're alone.

Oma's not alone.

Of course she's alone. Not all on her own, but she is alone.

Marie gets up and goes over to Gustl, who's reading the newspaper at the table. They've recently moved nearby. But I don't think Marie and Paula see any more of each other now. They take the same route to church, but Marie only takes it half as often as Paula.

There's no helping her, Gustl says. She has to do it for herself.

That's what I say, says Marie. It's different with your mother.

Why is it different?

She's got the two of you. And your father.

She should be in a good mood more often, then.

She can't help the way she is. She doesn't have it easy with her mother. It's a good thing she's gone back to work part-time. Take her mind off things.

And Paula can do the cleaning and cooking, says Gustl. She's good at that.

Of course she is, says Auntie Marie. And we always take her along to Montafon. We're happy to take her. *Mir drei alte Leit, mir kennet des gut miteinander*, she says, which means, literally, that the three old folks get on well, and really means that it's not all that bad.

Then she pauses.

For those three weeks, she says.

Sometimes, the memory of how it was mingles with a wish that came later: this is a good conversation I wish we would've had.

And you see the moon, a sickle above the woods. You hear the woodland animals, the long-eared owls, the wood pigeons and the tawny owls, and from the attic of the house you now live in whenever you want, you hear the hum of the hornet colony and the odd squeaks of the dormouse family. You hear animals in the dusk, jumping from the woods onto the roof, and you hear them scurrying around, you hear them scampering between the beams at night. You hear them gnawing. You hear them sliding down the insulation in the attic. You think they must be playing. You even hear them speaking, if you understand their squeaks and squeals as language, and you do. In the quiet of the night that settles over this house, their sounds are still loud. And although they disturb your sleep, their sounds are better than those that come out of muteness, better than the words that spring independently from silence, from speechlessness, from the expectation that someone will say the right thing. What matters, what ought to have been said long ago; or even what was never there and emerges as a word, a sentence, and somehow is exactly what was missing up to now. You've moved into a talking house, one that speaks out of the quiet and into the quiet.

She says she doesn't care. She's lived so long without anyone telling her who her father is. That's what my mother says. At some point you just want to leave it the way it is. She doesn't want to think about it any more, she says. She gets up, lights a cigarette, goes into the bathroom, opens the window and blows out the smoke. I sit down on the edge of the bath. When you're always getting teased, when the others are always picking on you, when they throw you in the stream and say, 'Go on, drown,' because they know you can't swim, and they hold your head underwater like they do with kittens and won't let you go until you say out loud that you're a bastard and all kinds of other things – all that's a punishment. She speaks loudly, only turning back to me occasionally as she exhales the smoke out of the window: Of course, you think you'll do it better one day. We talk about everything in this family, she says. I want us to talk.

I often follow her into the bathroom because she stays in one place when she smokes. She doesn't walk away. Otherwise, she often walks away when I want to talk to her.

I don't care now. I've finished with it, she says.

I hear the door to the flat opening.

She shakes her head. Not again, she says. She can't even stay up there for two hours at a time.

I hear my grandmother's stockinged thighs coming closer. Then she's standing in the bathroom doorway.

So, she says. She says it as a question, she says it the same way every time. My mother blows smoke out of the window.

I say nothing.

What are you two doing? she asks.

You can see what, my mother says.

She just wanted to ask if my mother will drive her to the chiropodist, later on.

Why can't you walk? my mother asks.

I don't feel up to it today, says my grandmother.

When? my mother asks.

In an hour, says my grandmother.

Alright then, my mother says.

I say nothing, although I'd like to say something to warm up their cold conversation, but I go absolutely quiet. As though I'd lost my voice. I think that I have to get away, that I can't stand it when they talk like this. I'm 17 and I get up and say I'm taking the bus into town later to get some books out. I know I won't feel good if I go out, but I won't feel good if I stay here either. I feel better when I roam around town looking for books I want to read. And when I keep an eye out for Charlie or someone else. I feel better when I read, because then I can't think about what is said here and what is not said.

My mother says: You've only just been to the library.

Doesn't matter, I say. I can only make it today, I've got practice tomorrow.

Always hanging about, says my grandmother.

You keep out of it, I say.

She lowers her head. Well then, she says, I'll come back down in an hour then.

My mother nods.

My grandmother stays put for a moment. She wants to say she doesn't deserve to be treated like this. She takes care of everything. I know she wants to say that, and she's right in a way. But she's never said it.

Well then, is all she says now, not looking at my mother and me. She puts her hand in her apron pocket but I can see that it's empty. She's left her rosary under the sofa cushion. It's praying in her absence. I'm the only person who knows.

Well then, my grandmother says again, her hand still in her apron pocket, and she still doesn't leave. Perhaps she wants to hear something more, something good.

See you later, Oma, I say.

Aren't you coming back up before you go? she says.

Yes, I am, I say.

She turns around.

That's all I need, says my mother as she hears my grandmother going up the stairs to her flat. I didn't want to leave the house again today.

But if she's not feeling well, I say.

She never says what's the matter, says my mother. You ask her what the doctor said, what the results were of the colonoscopy, and she says, wait and see. Wait and see, wait and see, says my mother.

I've got to get a cardigan, I say.

Have you really finished all those books? my mother asks.

Yes, I say. All of them.

I could have said: I won't take bribes. But I didn't say it, not once. I always saw it as compensation for everything she stole from me: my space, my secrets, my music, my joy, my private sphere, the possibility of masturbating without being caught, of bringing a boy home and up to my room without her standing outside eavesdropping or me expecting her to come in without knocking. I'm not allowed to lock the door. My grandmother always gives me money after her daughter's been rude to her and I didn't say anything nice in their presence. It's impossible for me – I can't put myself between my mother and my grandmother. But it's also not possible to say so. I stand there in her room and put the money in the pocket of my jeans. I don't need much more to buy the shoes I want. I stop at the sixth step from the top. I have to jump down from here so that nothing happens. So I'm not pregnant, and if I were pregnant the baby would fall out of me. I've never slept with a boy but I've dreamed I was pregnant, and it felt like I really was. I don't want to be pregnant. That's why I've been eating less for a few weeks, then the baby will get less food and won't be able to grow. I know that sounds pretty crazy so that's why I don't tell anyone, but I can't help thinking it. I think it all the time, and when it gets really bad I pray that it's not true. It often gets really bad.

Bye, I call into my parents' flat. Don't get back too late, my mother calls back.

I'm saving up for Danish shoes; they're called Danske Loppen. My friends wear them, the girls and also Charlie, who I've got a crush on because he looks like an indie rock star. They're expensive and you can only get them in one shop, my favourite shop. The owners' son and daughter go to my school. They're as blond as Danes. They wear the Danish shoes as well. Stef wears them, and who knows who else. You wear Adidas Sambas or Danske Loppen. Nothing else. I envy the shop owners' children, because I imagine their home is just as gorgeous as the shop. A bright and happy home. I bet they don't have a grandmother hanging around. I envy all my friends whose homes are noisy and cheerful, who have a room to themselves where no one is constantly butting in, or only their mothers. That seems like it would be easier to bear.

If my grandmother were still alive, she might say: It wasn't all like you're telling it, with us. I'm certain my perception doesn't tally with that of my grandmother; and certainly only partly with my mother's, not at all with my father's, because he was either working 60 hours a week or away on business. My father was a Sunday father. My brother was under neither my grandmother's special protection nor her observation, and also his room was on my parents' floor. Later, once I'd left home, he moved up to my grandmother's floor voluntarily. My grandmother didn't much like him bringing girls home with him, but it made her withdraw rather than crowd him. My brother and I had completely different childhoods. We had different parents. At least, their relationship to us and our relationship to them was completely different. It still is, these days. And even though I know that, I end up stumbling, hesitating whenever I think about it, asking myself if I'm allowed to write this story the way I'm writing it. I'm trying to reinvent real experiences as I write. For memory is inconstant; sometimes it casts images all around, sometimes single events occur to me, moments I then close in on as if through a zoom lens. I know their centre and I create, through writing, everything that takes me to that point, like a cat exploring its surroundings in expanding circles until it has created its own territory. My writing is what creates my territory. That's where I gather, stalk, hunt down and sometimes shoot.

When our small family was enlarged on special occasions and my grandmother sat among my father's brothers, their wives and my cousins, it was as though she consisted only of shame.

When faced with my other grandmother – my father's mother, a lady in a suit like Paula but who was as majestic as the Queen of England, a woman who received the family at the upper end of the long table in her living room, who resided at that upper end of the table, held court there, raised her voice and greeted everyone, allocated seats, showed great interest in her children's lives and asked her grandchildren about their grades – my Oma Paula would get smaller and smaller. When Oma Maria's laughter crowned her eyes with wrinkle garlands, Paula would sink entirely into herself alongside all that female force, curiosity, goodness and responsibility, but also imperious authority. Her eyes fixed on her fat knees, her handbag with the rosary inside it directly at her feet, she didn't even notice what was going on at the table, and you never knew – was she listening or was she in another world, was she praying? I would see that and think: Dear God, let me end up different from her. I saw the woman who was my grandmother staring holes in her knees and silently moving something around, something nobody was allowed to know about, just as nobody was to know the rosary was praying in her pocket, or she was praying the Rosary, not feeling the beads between her fingers. And yet someone always dared to speak to her, a cousin or one of my aunts. Someone would take pity on her and ask how she was, and she'd say: Oh yes, fine. And sometimes it occurred to her that she could ask them back how they were. And yourself? she'd say then, and for a moment she'd look up into their face; it was a quiet, gentle, cautious look, one without curiosity or expectation; and then she'd go quiet again. And sink into that quiet, the shame that seemed impenetrable, from which you'd involuntarily recoil. My grandmother wanted to disappear, in company. When I search my memory, there are only very few moments when I see her laughing; her laughter had no sound, it was a smile through closed lips. Her laughter had no voice. It was as though her laughter forbade itself, as if taking joy from life was forbidden, as if she had sinned so severely against her God that only prayer helped now. That's not what I thought then; it's what I think now. Perhaps she laughed when she was on her pilgrimages, perhaps there were places where she laughed; that was what I wished, hoped back then, because I would have wanted a better life for her than with us, than her life in a family where she wasn't happy, with a daughter she couldn't love because she reminded her of something or someone or of a humiliation, an indiscretion, day in, day out, and who didn't love her back because of that. The older I got and the more she hurt me and the more I rejected her and yet did love her nonetheless, the more I wished she had that: people and places

where she could be free for an instant. Perhaps Montafon was one of those places. Those weeks with her sister
Marie and Gustl.

My mother says: I wanted to get away as soon as possible,
lead a different life as soon as I could. An apprenticeship
meant money she could spend on clothes, because you had
to be well dressed to go to work. She met different people,
from the town and not her village, women she liked, and
at last she had friends who were emancipated enough not
to condemn her, my mother, for being a child without a
father or a father's name. She doesn't say that her friends
also acknowledged her beauty and appreciated her unfamiliar looks, but it's clear enough. Her sadness and her
simultaneous grace, her style, caught people's attention.
She said being in town every day gave her the opportu-
nity to meet my father. She was 16 when she fell in love.
She was lucky she was capable of love after so much un-
love. That's what I say. She met his father, she says, who
loved her instantly as though she were his own daughter,
who she loved instantly as though he were her own father.
You didn't earn a lot as an office assistant or a secretary,
she says, but it was enough to take home what her mother
needed, what she and my grandmother needed to tide
them over. And because that wasn't much she could still
go out for ice cream with Lili, whose name might actually be spelled with a double L and who became an important figure in our childhood, the most fun person in
our childhood. Lili and her children had a different life
to ours. Their home was lighter and brighter, noisier and
higher-pitched than ours. My mother laughed there like
she never did anywhere else. She was determined to get

married once she was 18, perhaps partly to get away from that place where she'd never wanted to be. And yet it was impossible to leave her mother behind.

My father loved my mother so much, even then, that he agreed to move into their first flat together along with her alcoholic, mentally ill, deliberately silent mother.

1938, it says on the back, and a word I can't decipher. The rest of the writing reads, as always, *FOTO FRANZ/ BIB-ERACH*, with the number *B 000 545*. But it's the photo that finally and yet only for a moment resolves the question – was the attractive man in so many of the photographs Karl Scheffold, my grandmother's fiancé? The man in the pale suit with short, wide lapels, a handkerchief, dark bowtie and dark shoes has his arm linked with my grandmother's the way a man only links arms with the most important woman in his life, and between ring finger and thumb glimmers something that might be a ring, almost certainly is the ring representing the first promise of the bond of marriage. And next to this man: my grandmother, calm and upright in a dark woollen dress, with a belt around her wide hips, a white sash-like stole over her shoulders, with a self-confidence she must have lost sometime later, after this Karl's death. Just like the laugh I first discover in one photograph from the same series, a laugh so happy, so loud that I can hear it in the photograph: my grandmother and her two sisters with bunches of primroses, elegant, more elegant than you'd expect of simple village people. The photo seems to capture an absolutely carefree moment. One like I always wished for my grandmother, yet one I could never imagine for her, not even in retrospect. Then I remember: in 1938 he was still alive, Ludwig Schwende, the man my grandmother kept in a little case like a treasure.

'The Photograph is *flat*, platitudinous in the true sense of the word, that is what I must acknowledge,' writes Roland Barthes in *Camera Lucida*. Only what's visible is evident. I see my grandmother happy with a very attractive man. It's nothing more than that.

More than any other, this picture prompts me to ask myself whether I have come any closer to her, to Paula. Photographs don't tell stories; they narrate the moment at which they were shot, that tiny escape. This is how it was at that moment, that's what photographs tell us. In this picture I find a woman, Paula, who once loved, who was loved, who laughed, was laughed along with, a woman capable of happiness in the midst of other people. I find my grandmother, I find the young Paula vividly alive; and as I feel joy at that, I can also sense the enormity of the catastrophe that must have caused her to change, ensured that nothing was left of that joy by the time she lived with us, when our two lives interlocked so balefully.

I sit at my desk watching *Bonanza*, remembering the moments shortly before *Bonanza* when my grandmother and I would get ready for the new episode, me singing along to the Rama margarine jingle and my grandmother moving her hand in her apron pocket, as she always did when nothing exciting was happening on *Bonanza*. I sit at my desk and find it very difficult to understand what I might have liked about it as a child.

Bonanza – at first, I was too young to watch it because there was shooting in it and loose women, and then I became part of the *Bonanza* family, which soon happened if you watched it regularly.

I watch a random episode I find on YouTube, and the man I think is Ben Cartwright says: How about man against man?

No weapons? the other man asks. OK.

Then put 'em down. That's the Ben guy or whoever he is.

And I try to go on watching but I can't help but drift from these images. The music is stronger than me, with such a powerful rhythm that even now, having not heard it for at least 30 years, I'm instantly back on the beige sofa next to my grandmother, precisely a hair's breadth away, and I don't know what I really felt while watching *Bonanza*. I keep remembering my grandmother's hand, moving in her apron pocket or behind her back against the sofa. I remember her hands praying, the rosary as a creature in her pocket or as an outsourced body part that had to be satisfied. I recognise Hoss and Little Joe and Ben Cartwright, I remember Hop Sing as my first TV chef, and I also remember doing drawings of Ponderosa. The name of the ranch still sounds full of promise to me to this day. My grandmother loved the show; she may well have seen every single episode shown on German television. I sat next to her because I had no idea where else I could have sat, or perhaps because it was nicer to sit next to her and watch *Bonanza* than to think bad thoughts that meant I'd have to pray. On *Bonanza*, everything was simple. They prayed too, but if you strayed from the right path, literally or metaphorically, you'd pretty soon end up with a bullet in your head.

You know that ox-eye daisies smell bad. They always have, but you remember how their white hue cast a spell on your grandmother. You remember how she loved carrying their white blossoms in front of her dark blue suit at the Corpus Christi procession, how you walked alongside her with a white basket full of colourful flowers the two of you picked the day before, how you skimped on scattering the petals, especially the coloured ones, as though the procession would never end or they were the most precious things in the world. How the two of you prayed at altars, how the silence grew light during prayers and processions. How you loved it. How your little child's steps were already big enough to keep up with your grandmother with her tight suit and poorly leg, how that went without saying. And then you find the photograph, the two of you in the fields on the day before Corpus Christi, and your own stare is no less dark than your grandmother's. As though it were infectious. And yet you recognise another expression on her face, a doggedness, her eyes without depth. As if everything concealed inside your grandmother needed protecting. And you understand: When she clenches her fist like you see in the photograph, no one will dare to break the silence. You want to feel that, you clench your own fist and this is what you feel: when you clench your fist, you're carrying the bunch of flowers in one hand and in the other, anger. If you release the fist, however, if you could release her fist, simply unfold her hand in the photograph, there would still be scepticism and grief in her face, but also the beauty of those white flowers. The picture doesn't show that they smell bad. Unfolding that anger – if only that were possible.

I write down everything I know, everything that occurs to me or that is substantiated as I go through the photos, through the memories I have of my grandmother Paula. I put it down in words as though paper, concentration, patience and analysis might form a real person. It makes me happy. The idea that taking stock – what do I know, what can I assume and what did I myself experience with my grandmother? – might make a person out of her for whom I might develop a certain understanding, perhaps even pity. Empathy, at least. An attempt, an experiment. It sometimes makes me feel almost euphoric. It doesn't solve the puzzle of my grandmother's deliberate silence, but it does solve that of the spell cast over our family, the silence we adopted.

Those womenfolk, always complaining about working, my grandmother says. We all used to work in the old days.

But didn't Hitler want women to stay at home with the children?

He wanted all sorts, he did! He had no idea. She dismisses him with a wave of her hand and purses her lips.

Lots of people liked him, I say.

Because he sorted things out, she says. But he messed everything up and all. People too.

What was it like in your village?

Another wave of the hand. What do you think? It was like it was everywhere.

What was it like?

Some people were good and some were bad.

Your brother Karl, did he like Hitler?

Oh, he was just like all boys of that age. He didn't understand what it meant to go to war.

And then?
You know that.
And what was it like for you in those days, life?
You always ask so many questions!

I have images. I have a smell. I have moments that are still horrific in my memory – thinking I'm going mad because I can't stop praying. The Lord God sees everything. I have to make amends: 20 Our Fathers; 50. I stuck two fingers up at her, I insulted her. Secretly. Another 20. I'll die if I don't pray. I can't stop. I feel sick. It must be appendicitis. Dear God, please let me wake up in the morning! Then I fall asleep.

The image I have of her now: sitting on the sofa, her hand buried in the right pocket of her apron, and I know what she's doing. Her hand is in perpetual motion underneath the flowered fabric. She's stroking, massaging. Sometimes she makes the sign of the cross when she thinks no one can see. If it were a photograph, no one could tell she was praying.

Once she's dead, the rosary doesn't come into my possession; it's not with her communion candle or the consecrated candles from Altötting. I don't know where it is.

My bedroom has two exterior walls. Another wall borders the bathroom and the hall. The fourth one is next to the kitchen. Because the room is at the very top of the house, the sloping ceiling limits how I can arrange the furniture. Outside my bedroom door, which I always close now, I hear my grandmother breathing, I hear her standing still,

I hear her feet shuffling on the carpet. I can't stand it any more. I begin to empty my shelves, taking all the books down and piling them in front of the door until the shelves are empty. I do the same with the next bookshelf. I empty my desk cupboard too. I barricade the door. It can't stay that way, I know that. But it makes me feel better. I put music on – I now have all of Simon & Garfunkel's records and my English grades have improved. I know most of the lyrics by heart. I'm lying on my bed listening to 'Bridge over Troubled Water' when the door handle moves. No, I shout very loudly. No. Then the piles of books fall into the room, and everything else too. I'm not lying on my bed any more. I feel tears pricking my eyes and I say: Can't you ever just leave me in peace?

She says: You've gone batty now! She presses her heavy body through the door, sending even more stuff tumbling over and into the room. Where there was once an ordered chaos, it now looks like an earthquake has struck.

Realising that tidying it up will be a nightmare, I start to cry. And then I scream: Go away, go away. She looks at me a while longer, I can feel it, I know her face when she looks that way – she purses her lips, and behind her glasses her eyes are fixed firmly on what interests her. I don't understand what's so interesting about me that she has to come into my room five times a day when I'm in there, and probably another five times when I'm not. I don't want to cry any more. I hear her moving.

You know it can't stay like this, she says.

It's my room, I say, still staring at my legs in my brand-new Wranglers.

I hear her leaving the room; I know she'll pray for me now and it makes everything worse.

As always, she doesn't close the door. She leaves it ajar.

I get up and close it. For the first time, I turn the key in the lock. I am alone.

I lie back down on the bed and survey the chaos. There's my huge collection of children's paperbacks, my Famous Five books, there are the slim yellow classics from Reclam, the rainbow of Suhrkamp paperbacks, Hermann Hesse and Max Frisch, Robert Walser and so on. They've slid below and beside school textbooks, comics, the teddies and dolls from the top of the shelves, and Bobby, the black doll I still have (to this day, in fact) and love the best. My dried roses are nothing but crumbs in among the mess. My gilt-edged hymnbook is face-down on the floor, pages splayed, and I'm sorry. Even though I feel like crying, I'm also glad, because it's the first time I've dared to lock the door to my bedroom.

Lying on my bed, I suddenly know exactly what I want to do. I lift the pickup arm off the record player and switch on my cassette recorder. I listen to Ralph McTell's 'Streets of London', turning up the volume until the room vibrates. I know the song off by heart, all that loneliness, and I sing along as I lift the mattress off my bed and push the bed frame along the sloping side to the other exterior wall, re-winding the song in between to listen again. I hear that my grandmother is outside the door, rattling the handle, calling my name and telling me to turn the music down, but that's exactly what I don't do. I keep going, I work on my bedroom all Saturday afternoon, listening to sad songs all the while, until my bed, protected by bookshelves, is as far away from the door and my grandmother as possible. Then I lie down on my back and look at the shelves all around me, and on them everything that belongs to me. I can't see the door from here, so I won't be seen the moment someone opens it. I don't know if I'm happy, probably not, and it's not just because of the sad music, but I am relieved. The record player is now placed so that I can easily reach it from my bed. I put the needle down on 'The Boxer', once, twice, I don't know how many times. At least as many as my grandmother has tried to come into my bedroom to-day. She's at church now, like every early Saturday evening. And when I realise that, I open the door to the hall and fetch the hoover. Then it occurs to me that no one has looked in on me all afternoon, even though my mother and brother must have got back from his football match hours ago. My father was out watching sports as well. On Sundays I have table-tennis games and tournaments, and sometimes I go to watch the men's team play on Saturdays.

My brother's team probably lost. I hoover the room and then I go downstairs. My mother and brother are watching the sports news on TV.

Hello, I say.

Hello, they both say. My mother looks up briefly; my brother is lying on the sofa in his tracksuit.

I've rearranged my bedroom, I say.

What, again? says my mother.

Can't you two be quiet? says my brother.

Didn't Oma say anything? I ask.

What should she have said? asks my mother.

Jesus, says my 14-year-old brother, can't you just be quiet?

VFB Stuttgart wins. FC Bayern does too. My mother and brother are happy.

Have you eaten yet? I ask, even though I know the an-swer.

When your dad gets back.

When's Dad getting back?

Soon.

And Oma?

She's gone on a pilgrimage.

I imitate the hand gesture I've just seen on the sports news. It's the one the footballers do when they've scored a goal. I make the gesture without a sound, but inside me it's loud.

So she won't be back until tomorrow morning, I say.

Tomorrow evening, my mother says.

I repeat the hand gesture. Yippie, I say quietly.

What? my brother asks, looking at me.

Nothing.

Why did I rejoice like that? Why?

That's what I keep thinking. It's absolutely impossible to stop. I'm sitting at the dinner table now that my father's home, and I'm not hungry. There's liver pâté on my bread and three gherkins on my plate. I like both a lot. But not now. I've been chewing at the slice of bread for minutes and it feels like it will be my fault if the bus my grandmother is on has an accident and they all die, or only my grandmother dies. I chew at my bread and liver pâté and the prayer begins in my mind: Dear God, don't let anything happen to Oma, dear God, don't let anything happen to Oma, dear God, don't let anything happen to Oma.

My brother did well in goal. Didn't let any shots in. They won. Dear God, don't let anything happen to Oma.

You were so hungry earlier, why aren't you eating now? my mother says.

I am eating, I say, but I can hardly say it because I can't let anything stop me from praying, and speaking and praying aren't really possible at the same time. My mother says nothing more, and my brother tells my father in great detail how he caught what shots, and my mother describes it in even more detail.

I try to eat the bread faster so I can go up to my room, so nothing happens.

I chew and swallow and put a gherkin in my mouth.

Can't you chew quietly? my brother asks.

I chew how I chew, I say. I've switched to letting Our Father run in my head, like listening to a record; I've practised it so many times. I can do it as long as I don't get interrupted, otherwise I have to start over from the beginning, and my guilt is only redeemed once I've prayed at least five Our Fathers in a row without mistakes. Usually, I have to pray the same number of Hail Marys afterwards.

What about you, my father asks. What did you do today? I can't answer because I'm up to 'and deliver us from evil', the point where I mustn't make a mistake at any cost, otherwise something will happen.

What's the matter? my father asks.

One, I think. One down.

I rearranged my bedroom, I say.

Again? says my father.

This time for good, I say.

Aha, he says. Anything else?

Nothing else. It's better now, I say.

Anything else? my father asks, looking around the table. Our Father who art in heaven, don't let anything happen to Oma.

I see my grandmother's sad, sunken face with its delicate bird-feather wrinkles, and on it her unhappiness that the only person in the whole house to whom she was a little close for a happy period of 10 years, or even longer, wants nothing more to do with her. Her sadness is oppressive and gets more oppressive with every year, because I close myself off to her more with every year.

In my imagination, she's sitting opposite me. I watch her hand in her apron pocket and wait. I think of beetles with iridescent backs, large and almost black or dark green with tiny furry feet, and I think of the snake in the window of the chemist's shop, and how its throat – when it swallows the hamster it gets fed once a day – moves exactly the same way as my grandmother's hand in her apron pocket. I like going to the chemist's window and I always get goose pimples because what happens there is real. It's different from watching television. And now it occurs to me that I used to stand at that shop window in the exact same way as I'd sit by my grandmother, watching and waiting. The TV was always on, and I remember the washing powder ads, the Rama and Nivea ads, and all the cigarette ads because smoking was still allowed back then. And I remember how her hand would move faster when the wanted terrorists Christian Klar and Ulrike Meinhof were on the news, when a dead body had been found in the boot of a car, absolutely real and not all that far away. Her hand would move differently than with the bodies on *Bonanza*, which turned into Ken and Barbie when they died, forever beautiful. And how she'd stare at the big cathode-ray screen from Loewe, Loewe Opta, the same brand as her radio, and the same shade of brown. I remember realising for the first time that she wasn't actually seeing anything. Realising she was looking inwards, and as I look at her and wonder whether she has to concentrate while she does the thing with the beads, I want to stand up and leave. I want to leave because I already know it will get worse with every minute I stay there, with every minute the room fills with more of the God she's beseeching, and it gets more and more threatening because I can do more and more things wrong. And although I know that, although I know only praying can help against this God, who is by no means a kind God, I stay where I am and stare at her hand in her apron pocket. Before a commercial break, there's a short cartoon, which I'm too old for really but I still find funny when I'm not sitting next to her. And today, I wonder whether I could have said anything to object to that hand in her apron pocket. But words failed me then. And then this image comes: the two of us sitting in that room, over and over again, even though I'd wanted to creep past her door on the way to my bedroom. I couldn't do it; it was a duty I had to fulfil. Her feet shuffling under the table, and the way her still heavy body would sit on the sofa, and the way she breathed, and the way she looked, as if there was something right you could do for her, something good, except that you were too bad to do it. That's what I remember. The way we sat facing each other, both secretly praying, and the only difference that still existed was that I didn't have a rosary, that I grew boundless in my prayers, bound to no law. I remember her mute presence in my room when I came home from school, I remember sensing she'd been in there again. All the traps I had set told me she'd been looking for something or other again, in the drawers and under the bed and in the wardrobe. Records and exercise books, Hermann Hesse and Max

Frisch became secrets because she looked for the secret she was hiding in all of my things. As though she might find it outside of herself, in me. As though I were her. I remember her denying her secret by insisting I have one, and I remember believing I was going crazy, in my bed behind the shelves, and thinking I'd die boarded into the corner of the room. I remember how dark it was and how I had to refuse everything in that house, fight everything off, my grandmother most radically of all.

Ten years later, I sleep in that room again. My grandmother is still alive and I'm on my way to Italy. Sitting next to a truck driver my father found to take me along, on the ferry across Lake Constance, I take my sponge bag out of my backpack and open it, and holy pictures fall out of it, like some foreign currency she has secretly smuggled into my luggage. I start to cry.

There were the dresses she'd been given, cast-offs from a cousin or someone else, not rags but not dresses she'd wish on us. You could wear them, of course you could, my mother says. There was nothing else. There was nothing nice, never even a hint of abundance. There was no money or none available, because everything went on brandy. She didn't say that when I was a child. Everything was old, my mother said.

And I understand why my mother was dead set against me wearing second-hand clothes or the old cardigan I unearthed in the cellar and thought was chic. And now I understand my mother's French skirts and trousers, blouses and shoes and coats and jackets that I saw her wearing when I was a child and later a teenager. I understand why she taught herself to sew when money was tight for a while because of the new house. I understand why I was supposed to wear homemade trousers instead of used jeans, which seemed so much more appealing to me or, looking back, cooler. But cool wasn't a word in my childhood. Cool was not something for shy people, and I was shy. My mother's unapproachable beauty, no matter what she wore, was cool. The bastard was the young Parisienne in the village.

I remember my grandmother's deliberate silence when she had to come along to a family therapy session once, twice or perhaps even three times. Alright, if you insist. And like the rest of my family, my grandmother felt I was placing a burden on them all, made me feel it was my fault that they were all supposed to talk about how we communicated in the family and what my starving sickness might have to do with them.

My grandmother sitting on an armchair, handbag alongside her, hair freshly set, staring at her lap. I don't know where she's put her rosary but I'm sure she has it with her because she never leaves the house without it, certainly not to go to a place she doesn't know. The family therapist asks her if she can imagine doing something that would be good for me. He doesn't speak in dialect. To my grandmother, people who don't speak in dialect and are doctors too are either heroes or fools. She says nothing, and when he asks her if she understood the question, she says: *I wois au it* – I don't know. She looks bitter and sad. I'm ashamed. And I wait. Something has to happen, surely. The doctor asks my mother if she has an idea for something my grandmother could do for me. My mother replies very quickly that she doesn't know. And yet I know she knows it as well as I do. She could keep out of my room, let it be my space. She could stop watching me like I'm a dangerous insect. When the doctor asks my brother, he says he doesn't know either. My father has no idea. On the way home, my brother says it's my fault they have to go through all this crap. My grandmother says she doesn't know what good it's supposed to do. My father says all it does is rock the boat. My mother says it might be good for something, maybe. It's dark already; I sit on the back seat by the window and don't even try to hold back the tears running down my cheeks. And then I feel my grandmother's hand slipping into the pocket of her suit jacket. I feel the creature in her pocket next to me, I know she's praying for us. At breakfast the next day, she says: That fool's complicated questions won't get us anywhere.

I tell her he's not a fool. I'm 18. I'm moving out soon, I say.

Silence all round.

I start making my own clothes. The small sewing machine often tangles the threads, and then I have to pluck everything apart with much swearing and effort. It's the sewing machine my mother always used, made by Elna, and I love it because it brings me independence. I find nice fabric and learn how to make trousers, and that means I wear the best trousers anyone can wear. I don't need my parents' money or their advice. Sitting at the sewing machine in my room, I hear nothing from outside; the rattle of the motor is louder than my grandmother's footsteps, louder than my parents' voices as they argue downstairs. Since I've been living in my room with the machine, I've felt at one with myself for the first time. It has become my pet, an even better one than the record player. When my grandmother puts her head around the door, without knocking as always, to say it's late and I should go to bed, I don't react. I'm sewing. My grandmother comes closer but she's on the other side of the machine and the machine protects me. I speed down the trouser legs with the needle, I put my foot down as though I could sew my grandmother into the ground. My grandmother shakes her head and asks what I'm making, and I go on saying nothing. I'm making something. I know I am and soon she'll see.

I'm living in another town now and only come back occasionally. Sitting on the armchair in her living room, I don't ask about her; I ask about life in general. I play the careful conversation partner – I want to know everything but I know she doesn't want to tell me anything, or she can't, but I feel like I might manage to sneak up on specifics, on her, so I say it like this: What was it like all alone, a woman with a child, after the war?

And she hesitates and then she says: You needed some comfort.

And she twists the rosary in her apron pocket. I see it but I don't look at it; I know I'm not supposed to see it.

And I ask: Where did you find comfort? And I know that's not a good question.

What were you supposed to do, all alone? she says, looking over at the budgie, another Bobby because Hansi, who came after the last Bobby, has died in the meantime. Right, Bobby? she says, and she barely raises her head, looking out through the blinds at the slatted world outside, and she says, I don't even want to think about it. It wasn't easy.

And I wait and perhaps I look slightly too expectant, trying to act like a journalist but hoping she doesn't think I'm intruding on her, and I sense her withdrawing again as she says: What can I say?

And I say: But you didn't have any money. What did you live on?

The creature in her apron pocket shifts, as if it could help, and she says: It got easier later. But when the war was over... and then she falls silent and the creature moves, agitated, and I look carefully to see if I can tell whether she's saying an Our Father or a Hail Mary, but I can't see anything so I don't know which prayer she's got to by now. As if I ever knew, I think, and try not to look at the hand in the apron. I wait until she says, at last: You're left there with nothing.

But you must have lived off something, I say.

There were the geese and... And later I did cleaning. I never learned a trade.

I realise I have no idea how things worked back then. I say: But you did go to school.

Yes, I went to school, the village school. What can I say? And she descends into her silence, which isn't as bad this time, perhaps because we've spoken now. Perhaps because she's glad I'm speaking to her again.

It's silent, then. I think she might say something more, and outside I hear a blackbird calling loudly. It's the one I think I know; blackbirds can live quite a few years. It's a familiar voice from the garden. But when I see a starling through the slats, perching on the neighbours' bird box, I grow uncertain for a moment. My grandmother will turn to face the starling too, I know that, and we'll watch the birds together. But does it matter? And yes, she looks over, lost in contemplation, her hand still working away, and it is one of the few moments when I can love her without that spark of ambivalence, without thinking she ought to reflect more and tell more of her story and without wondering where the images are that she refuses to reveal. We are silent together. It's good.

And then she says: He wanted it that way. Him up there. And her jaw makes a small motion, pulling her double chin back and tightening the skin of her neck, and she looks much less old.

The professor I worked for at university had a friend in Italy. A famous sculptor in his country, he made musical objects out of stone and invited people who were artists or wanted to become artists to his village, San Sperate in Sardinia, to continue the local mural tradition. My professor thought it might be good for my Italian, so he arranged for me to stay with Pinuccio Sciola. Can she paint? the artist must have asked my professor, and he said yes. I was in my late 20s, a mature student, and I drove to Sardinia alone in an old Opel Corsa my mother had passed on to me, then across the island to the artist's village, and everyone I met on the island seemed to know him so well that I thought they must be related, at least by marriage. Everyone loved him and no one had anything but praise for him. I was looking forward to the weeks in his village and his workshop. It was afternoon by the time I arrived, and I somehow made my way through the gate and found the artist in the kitchen, chopping tomatoes and mixing them with garlic and basil. I said: I'm the student from Tübingen, and he looked at me with his big dark eyes and said: *O, ma non è una bionda!*

That was the point when I sensed things wouldn't go well between us. About two days later, he told me I had to move out of the room next to his workshop. He had another little room for me and he needed mine over the next few days for other guests. At that point, I was painting a kind of graphic novel on a wall in the middle of the village, a love story in 16 episodes. The characters were matchstick figures that learned to fly in the end, and then made a break for it. Each of them separately. No idea what gave me that idea. I was working on the wall every day, and in the evenings I'd eat with Sciola and sometimes other guests, but he never talked to me. He liked the wall I was painting so much, though, that he offered me another one when the first wall was done, provided I moved out. If not, I'd have to leave. That was all he said. Being used to people not speaking, I thought I had to put up with it, and I immersed myself by day in my work on the wall of a house belonging to an elderly woman and her son, who had two small children. They were very happy and pleased to have me, feeding me greasy pastries and bringing me drinks. When I got back to the workshop on my fifth evening, the artist's brother-in-law, or whoever it was, was waiting to pick me up – it was time for me to move. We got into his car and drove around the village until we got to a very basic worker's house, at least that's how I remember it, and out came an ancient, nun-like woman with thick glasses. She was friendly and invited me into the house, and inside it looked exactly like the woman looked, and she said she was sure we'd get on very well, but I thought that was highly unlikely.

From the moment I met her I felt like crying, my chest so tight I could barely speak. I didn't understand what was happening to me until that evening, when I lay beneath a very realistic Jesus looking down at me from his cross in a gloomy chamber, between rustling sheets that smelled slightly dusty, and felt like I was being watched.

I had gone so far away from home, to a place that had nothing in common with my origins, only to find myself in the house of my bigoted Catholic grandmother, and I couldn't even be angry with her because she wasn't my grandmother. The past had caught up with me, there in San Sperate with Pinuccio Sciola's aunt, who wanted to watch TV with me just like my Oma always wanted. Stay here, my grandmother had said. *Perchè non rimani?* the aunt asked, patting the spot next to her on the sofa. There was a Catholic mass on TV.

Can I eat at Sciola's place? I asked the brother-in-law, or whoever it was who had brought me to the aunt, and the brother-in-law said: No, you can eat here.

I finished my mural the next day, having prayed a lot during the night so nothing would happen to me in this place where I could barely sleep, because I felt the need to fight off the spirits of the dear Lord and my grandmother even in my sleep, because I felt like I was going mad in the tiny room, which took on a ghoulish darkness in the night, after the aunt had walked around it with an incense burner to cleanse all my belongings of the world's evils. I had panic attacks during the night, praying not to go mad, praying to God even though I was insanely angry with Him and my grandmother, but I had no other choice. If I had cursed Him instead, something would have happened, that certainty was buried too deep. On a later occasion, I once blew out a holy candle in a chapel on Tinos so that I could lie in my sleeping bag in the dark. Nothing happened other than a woman lighting it again early the next morning. But in the Italian aunt's house, I did everything I had never wanted to do again: I prayed like I'd had to pray in my parents' house.

I left the next day. Lost in Sardinia, lost in my own apostasy.

Sometimes I wonder whether I could have been more forceful and stubborn about my questioning. And why I never dared to ask: Are you satisfied with your life? Satisfied, not happy.

I didn't ask myself at the time whether anyone ever really wanted to know how that life came about, the life my grandmother led – was forced to lead? Or whether anyone else ever tried to understand it. I do wonder whether I could be more forceful about my questioning now, into the vacuum that surrounded her, especially during her prayers. Was a mother only a proper mother when she had a father by her side, and otherwise a whore? Perhaps the options were whore or wife, goddess or witch. I didn't ask myself where her bitterness came from and why she became an alcoholic, became a drinker; for a long time, I didn't even know she'd been one. I loved the woman who was my grandmother, but there was a long period during which I hated her.

Later, once I've stopped hating her again, once all I know is that she made my life incredibly difficult, made our life difficult; later, once I'm beginning to question that, once I think that my parents ought to have accepted responsibility for our lives, for love in our home and against the silence, once I've started thinking about all this, I say to her: Say something – you're going to die soon! Your dear Lord would want you to. She's lying in her hospital bed, asleep or on the way to the place where she's yearned to go for years now. Or at least, I believe she would have long since arrived in her heavenly kingdom if she hadn't been so afraid of dying. But it's not up to her to decide any more. Death will come, it's already perched on the edge of her bed. Her little head is buried deep in the pillow, her blue-rinsed hair less blue than usual. She hasn't been able to get it done for a while now. Who do we make ourselves beautiful for? I should have asked her that. Do you have the image of a person in your mind, a person you love or once loved? Does he still see you when you look at him? I'm 30 years old and I stare, silent, at the bed she's lying in, her eyes closed, a drip in her arm, and because she's asleep or in a strangely distanced state, the bed is silent back. Not even her breath speaks. There's a bad smell, as always in hospitals, but it smells worse here, sweet and sickly. I feel watched. The other woman in the two-bed room has her family around her. They're talking. Their grandmother too. They're laughing and their grandmother laughs with them. I try to remember whether my grandmother ever really laughed out loud when she was with me and my family. The sweet-smelling other old woman hasn't sunk so deep inside her pillow. I shift closer to my Oma Paula's bed so she can hear me. If she can still hear anything, that is. Life's not very good when you don't know where you come from; something is missing. Say something, I say. I say it so quietly that only she and I can hear it, I say it slightly louder than how she used to pray. Of course, she says nothing. She's never said anything about it; why should she say something about it now? Are her nostrils trembling a little more? Her face has grown pointed, but it doesn't have more wrinkles; her skin still looks delicate and soft, and I mustn't let myself think about how I would lie with my face next to hers, pressed against the woodchip wallpaper on those nightmare nights, or else I'll cry. A fine layer of fluff grows on her chin. You don't have to tell me, I say quietly. You don't have to tell me anything, just say his name! That would be a whole lot. Or say it to your daughter, at least! I whisper. The family around the other bed look over. I get up, walk around the bed and open her bedside drawer. There it is, the mother-of-pearl beads white and shimmering, the silver cross glinting. I don't know whether to touch it, whether I'm allowed to, and if I put it in her hand then everyone will see it. She might drop it. Someone might take it. I close the drawer, leaving the holy thing where it is. I'd like to take her hand but I'm unsure. Then I change my mind and put the rosary in her hand, the hand close to me beside her body. I have to open her fingers slightly but when she feels the rosary she closes her fingers around it. I feel watched, doing something so intimate it seems almost forbidden, and when I turn around I see the family from the other bed looking at me, father, mother and a blond angel with a runny nose, about seven years old. My friend Stephan sometimes says: Fuck the fuck off. We sit outside the uni building and drink vending-machine coffee out of cups without saucers. We know each other because we both write. Stephan likes Metallica. I don't. We're not a couple, just buddies. Stephan never says that thing to me. He doesn't say it the way you might interpret it. When he says it, it sounds more like: Yeah, baby! I don't say it now, though; I turn back to my grandmother and check whether her hand is moving, but it's not; only her fingers are firmly closed around the beads and I think it might be that my grandmother has just perfected the art of praying the Rosary and doesn't even have to run the beads through her fingers to know whereabouts she is in her prayer. I look at my grandmother's blueish fingers, which have grown thin like she has, and I'm very glad when I see that she's not letting go of the beads, she's holding tight. She's praying.

That's the granddaughter, I hear the sweet-smelling diabetes lady say, in a loud voice. She's only been once, she adds.

I think about whether to take my grandmother's hand and hold the rosary with her, but my very thinking about it tells me I'd rather not. I sit there with my grandmother, both silent together. But it's still not like it always was.

When my grandmother is buried it's November. It's in the afternoon, and as we stand at the grave and the coffin is lowered, the sun comes out suddenly and a single ray of light lands on her grave. I'm glad, I'm so glad it's as if a miracle has happened, but it's just me being happy that my grandmother's body is getting a little more warmth on its way into the dark earth.

When the communion is over at my grandmother's funeral, my Protestant father strides out of the pew in response to some sign that he interprets as the end of the service. My brother follows him and so do I. By the time we're walking down the broad aisle of the baroque church to the exit, I notice that my mother hasn't come with us, nor anyone else. Standing in the churchyard, it's clear it was a misinterpretation. My father frets about what people will say, what my mother will say. I tell him we'll just go to Oma's grave and tidy the flowers there so that it looks like we had a reason to leave the service early. When the funeral procession comes out of the mortuary chapel, we act as busy as we can.

After the funeral, my mother says: Paula would have shaken her head at you three and said she tried everything but it was no use: you don't even know when church is over. Then she laughs. It's a conciliatory laugh. That's the second good moment at my grandmother's funeral. And it's the first one that makes me cry.

When I pick up the church and turn it upside down or simply shake it, snow falls around it. Then sacred Altötting is covered in snow. It snows a while longer, even after I put the church back in its place on top of the radio. I can't imagine my grandmother bought the snow globe for herself but who would have given her such a thing? She had no time for poetic things, my grandmother; they weren't useful. Perhaps someone in Altötting gave her a souvenir, or something nice happened there and she bought it out of gratitude. I feel a sense of melancholy when I occupy myself with all the things, pictures and objects, people in photos who I don't recognise or know anything about. Again and again, I ask myself whether I did something wrong. Again and again, I feel the sense of threat that emanated from my grandmother, again and again I know she made my life difficult. Again and again, I'm sure in the end that she didn't mean to. I know there was no way to make her happy, and if you caused her pain she wouldn't show it for a long time. Up until she could no longer hide her sadness. Until she consisted of nothing but sadness. In reality, I have no idea who she was. Or what would have happened if she had let someone get close to her, what would have happened if someone had managed to love something out of her, live something out of her. It didn't happen. Looking back, it seems as if she'd recognised something in me that was so close to her that it scared her. So much so that she had to pursue what pursued her, that she had to keep checks on me like she kept checks on herself. To her, my life seemed under threat, when really it was her threatening it.

It's good that this little red candle is burning. This far back, there are rarely other people about; it's lonely so close to the field, mice scurrying across the gravel in the dark, the wind breaking against the wall, and if you only wait long enough a piece of sandstone will crumble away. I can already hear the sound, the quiet rot trickling down the wall. As though something were moving in all the nooks and crannies. You can't hear it in the grave. In summer, lizards soak up the sun on the pale rough surface of the wall, even in the dusk. My grandmother lies facing west, the same position her bed faced, between the early and late sun.

It's your birthday today, I say.

Why don't I say: It would be your birthday? You'd be turning 95 today. I know you probably wouldn't have wanted to get that old. We're only attached to life when we have something to lose. I pause for thought. How can I know whether there wasn't something, after all, that kept my grandmother alive, even if it was only that she couldn't leave her secret behind.

Anyway, it would have been your birthday today.

The idea of talking to the dead is not new, nor is the need to do so. We always speak to those who have left us, no matter whether they're alive or dead. Because we don't have answers, never do, or because new questions have come up since our parting. I have always had the same questions for my grandmother. But they've become more specific over time, or they have spread out inside me.

A grave is a place where chronology is cancelled out. The difference between today and yesterday, when the person in the grave was alive, becomes irrelevant. Someone is lying in the grave and is as close as ever, but dead. There are no answers from the grave. The grave doesn't speak. My mother takes care of the plot. It looks like the other graves here. The fact that I come here now and then and talk to my grandmother is a secret.

I say, do you remember how Dad, my brother and I left the church too early at your funeral because we didn't know there was more to come? And everyone stared at us, just because Dad's a Protestant and we had no idea because we'd never been to a Catholic funeral, my brother and I. Remember that? And then Mum said to us: Oma would have said it was typical, you three don't have a clue.

How that helped me to make my peace with you.

And I think that now I'm telling her this myself, it might make her laugh. I think she's glad to hear it, perhaps even happy.

And because this is the first time I'm glad to be standing by my grandmother, here at her grave on this November afternoon, I take the little brush out of the holy water container and splash a little of it on my grandmother, and for the first time in a long while I make the sign of the cross with my thumb, like she always would, very fast so that no one would see it.

You were still alive when I was travelling in Greece with Frank, it was late summer and because we had no money we slept outside most nights. We would rather have stayed in monasteries but we didn't find any. And one night, it was late, we didn't know where to sleep. The sea was rough, the Meltemi was blowing, the tide was high, and we found a chapel not far from a little road. Out of the wind, it was beautiful because it was suddenly quiet. It was just too bright to sleep, somehow, because several sanctuary lamps were burning and the light shone all the way into our corner, into our eyes, our sleeping bags, our tiredness. We got up and blew out the candles and laughed. It was a relief that I could laugh about that. It was night time, we were tired, we needed to sleep. It was dark and good.

In the morning, the sanctuary lights were burning again. I know you would have told me off if I'd told you, and threatened that the dear Lord would punish me for it if I didn't go to confession right away. Now I'm confessing to you, I say. I'm still alive, I say. I didn't even need to pray.

I only visit my grandmother's grave in secret. I still can't manage to bridge the gap between her and my mother. My mother wouldn't understand what I'm doing there. I don't even know it myself. Taking leave, perhaps, still saying goodbye.

And I imagine putting on one of her aprons, sitting down in her armchair by the window, Bobby or Hansi hopping around next to me in his white cage, feathers ruffling, sand rustling as he lands, bells jingling as he hops up again. He's agitated. He'd like to fly.

When I say, 'Be quiet, Bobby,' he goes quiet, and when I reach into my apron pocket I find the rosary. I begin to pray. I pretend I know the rules of the rosary well, as though I know what to do, but really my fingers only wander from one bead to the next: small, small again, small again, until at last I hit a big bead, and I keep a close eye on what happens to the fabric of the apron pocket, how it moves. Does it look like it used to when my grandmother did it, or does it look different? I think about the differences between inside and outside. I have to stop paying attention to what is visible from the outside; the experiment is only about what must have gone on inside my grandmother when she sat there, one hand in her apron pocket, praying. For hours. For days. I'm alone, I close my eyes, Bobby cheeps and tweets and makes all kinds of noises and I look for a thought that might torment me, because I think my grandmother was constantly occupied with thoughts that tormented her, and those are easy to find: thoughts in which the person you love most leaves you, those are the worst thoughts you can have, because they scare you the most, perhaps more than the thought of cancer that might recur. If the cancer comes back and the person you love is still there, then the cancer has less power. If the person you love is gone when the cancer comes back, then it's an attack on a weak system with no support. So being abandoned, being left is the far worse disaster, at least to my mind. And as I'm thinking about that, I begin to pray: *Hail Mary, full of grace, the Lord is with thee*, and I drift into the mantra of my childhood years: *Dear God, don't let the cancer come back, and don't let me be abandoned, please don't let me be abandoned, and please don't let the cancer come back, etc.,* and although it's incredibly childish it goes on in my head, and I imagine that's the way it must have been: that my grandmother prayed herself into a mantra, that she simply prayed away every thought that tormented her, so often until it was gone and only words remained. Only prayer. So the only point of prayer is that it replaces words that are hard to bear with words that are easier to bear, ideas that are hard to bear with devotionals, and these are only good for lifting curses you believe yourself to be plagued with.

I'm going to give up the burial plot, my mother says on the telephone. I can't do it any more. She hears the silence at the other end. She doesn't know where that silence is calling from. Where has her daughter gone so quiet?

I take pity on her. I'm hanging up the washing, I say.

It's just too much for me, she says, when my body's aching all over.

I understand. But I don't want the grave not to be there any more.

Where will she go?

She doesn't answer. She hates it when her daughter still asks the same questions as when she was a child.

She's been dead more than 15 years, she says in the end.

Her bones are still there, I don't say.

You never go to the graveyard anyway, she says.

That's not true, I say.

But how often though?

And what do they do with the worms and the maggots? They practically are my grandmother now. That's what I think and I know she would say: Can you stop behaving like a child and act your age? And she'd be right.

And what will happen to the gravestone? I ask.

My mother doesn't know what it looks like where I'm hanging up the washing; she's never visited, even though I've invited her several times.

I don't care what happens to the stone, she doesn't say, but I hear it nonetheless.

I say: There are names on it!

I don't know what she says in reply.

Do you want to reuse the stone?

I don't need a stone, I want to be cremated, my mother says.

Stop it, I say; I don't want to hear that.

She can hear me shaking out a pillowcase, I know she can.

I've got to go, I say. Think it over again!

I know she's wondering whether her daughter was crying. I can't help it either, she says to the dog jumping up at her legs. She leans down to him: What would we do without you? I know she says that.

The dog licks her chin; he can't get any higher than that, he's a small dog. He's the smallest they've ever had. It's a good thing they have him.

When the man whose presence doesn't bother me at all when we're both writing in the same room, the man with whom I swim lakes and climb mountains, with whom I started surfing at an age when you learn only slowly, with whom I'm learning to read the sea, with whom everything is always better merely because we've got each other, even when we happen to be miles apart – when this man asks me if I want to marry him, and we really decide to do it, a year later, I call my mother.

Save the date, I say. Don't go on holiday – we're getting married.

On the other end of the line, a deep breath in, a big breath out. The last thing she says: I'm going to have to digest that.

Then nothing happens for more than four weeks.

To this day, I don't know exactly what my mother had to digest.

For two years, I didn't look at the wedding photos taken by my husband's then 14-year-old son, who has become my son too, a little. I didn't look because they never got moved from one computer to the other or because the real memories were stronger than the desire to look at the photos again. The boy's a very good photographer, though, and he took shots of all the people at the wedding with great devotion. And when I look at the photos, I see my mother gazing at us, my husband and me, with the same look on her face as my grandmother in one of the photos I now possess, staring at my beautiful mother and my father. It's not a good look. It's not a friendly look. Not a benevolent one, not one you'd like to meet. Yet it's not critical either. I haven't the slightest idea what resentment, what objection that look is feeding on. It's a look you'd rather not have seen, because it won't ever let you go. And because the deliberate silence has since settled around the marriage issue, I don't ask about it. We don't talk about it, we stay silent and avoid being close. When we do speak, we're friendly to each other, and yet helplessness still rises within me, and grief; and the feeling, the legacy of that silence, that muteness that rests upon us, has the weight of a stone.

Silence is carried down generations. When everything that has to be said is not said, and everything that would be better left unsaid is spoken. You sink into yourself; your thoughts drift across the white tablecloth, through the clatter of knives and forks on plates, the round movements of the ladle in the spoutless sauce boat. You gaze at the bowl of homemade *spätzle*, the pork loin in the bowl alongside it, the salad. You look at the arrangement on your plate, the egg-coloured pasta next to the chestnut brown. You can be right there and want nothing. You think: My life is elsewhere and that makes it better than before, because you can keep the fear at bay, whatever you're afraid of but above all dying, the fear that always comes when you're here, the fear of death. The fear that life might end overnight, your own or that of one of your family members at the table. You always factor in mortality when you inhabit this muteness, as though death and the unsaid were one and the same; the dying inherent to not speaking, the loss of vitality as you observed it in your grandmother. You know that in this house, this fear is sometimes the other side of anger, fear of anger. Anger at everything that has never been said, anger at your own inability to ask in such a way that prompts answers, anger at the others, who are silent in the same way she was silent, and as you are silent along with them now. The deliberate silence is like a worm, a slug, not a creature of importance but one that devours everything, destroys it. So you sit at the table and say the food is delicious, and your mother complains as usual that something's not right, because there's always something that hasn't turned out as well as she wanted.

You say: No, it's delicious. Because it really is very good.

You're guest and stranger at the same time, you're sitting at this table and thinking of her, Paula, the way she sat there for more than 20 years, attempting to be a good grandmother year after year, to be a good mother over and over, attempts that failed, just like your attempts to be a good daughter. But because you know in a few hours' time you'll be in a place where it's lively, a place where you feel like yourself, where you know why you're there, that's why you stay sitting quietly. You hear your brother and your parents talking and you remember your grandmother on her chair, the dog always wanting to be close to her at mealtimes even though she was strict, even though she was a woman who disapproved of feeding animals at the table. Perhaps the dog protected her. The dog that was the only one allowed to get close to her, because she would talk to him, the way people talk to dogs; she was frank with him. The dog and her God were good. And as you sit there you become aware that where you're sitting was her place. You're the one on the margins now, you're the one who doesn't speak. And yet you want to.

Translator's Note

The story of *Paula's* translation is a long one. I first came across Sandra Hoffmann's book when it won the Hans Fallada Prize, a German literary award for fiction with a political and social background. The premise of the book fascinated me and I swiftly got hold of it. What a devastating story, so beautifully told!

Sometimes translators read differently to other people. If I find myself trying to translate as I go along, that's usually a good sign – that I want to take co-ownership of the book, put it into my own words. Here, though, there were two major hurdles. What to do with the Swabian dialect, so integral to the narrator's emotions. And what on earth to do with the essential word *schweigen*, a notion that doesn't exist in such compact form in English and yet crops up in the very first line.

The first step, though, was to invite Sandra Hoffmann to spend a week working with translators at the British Centre for Literary Translation's summer school in 2018. I effectively passed on the conundrums to a fantastic group of emerging and early-career literary translators, who had five days to think deeply about them with Sandra's advice and support. That was how the idea came about to retain some of the Swabian in the dialogue. When the groups read their excellent work aloud on the final day, the dialogue worked! And thankfully, having Sandra on hand helped us to decipher the meaning very easily and hear the sound in her own voice.

There followed a search for a UK publisher for a full translation. This has never been my strong point, but in my defence, it is difficult. Presses have restricted budgets and only so many slots, and taste varies wildly. Whatever the case, I didn't find anyone who shared my massive enthusiasm. Ho hum, another one bites the dust. At least I don't have to find a solution for *schweigen*.

Except then I had the idea of setting up an English-language imprint with a German publisher. Having found a sufficiently adventurous press, Voland & Quist, part of our initial conversation was my wish-list. *Paula* was at the very top of that list.

I'll skip a bit because this is a translator's note, not an emerging publisher's note. Suffice to say, I did now have to find a solution for *schweigen*. The summer school participants had tackled it and found a very elegant way around it – after much discussion – but I felt I had to start anew and I wasn't happy with anything I came up with.

I don't really believe in the concept of 'untranslatable words'. What we have to do is find ways to explain them or paraphrase them that don't blow a hole in the original text. Likewise, 'untranslatable books' demand creative translations, reworkings, bold steps. Ownership on the part of the translator, if you will. It's always an implicit part of our work to help readers understand a book's cultural setting, by choosing words carefully and occasionally making discreet additions – inserting a gloss, to use the technical term. Saint Jerome, the horribly misogynist patron saint of translators, was a great fan of glosses in his biblical translations.

Could I do that in the first sentence? The German is:
Schweigen ist anders als still sein.
Rendered in the words English offers us, the literal translation would be something like:
Silence is different to being silent.
Which doesn't cut it, does it?
After hours of fiddling with those first six words, and after moving on so I'd at least get started on finding the right voice for Sandra's book, I returned to the beginning at the end. I came up with a very brief explanation for the word *schweigen*: 'deliberately remaining silent'. And I built that into a sentence and a half in the tone I had found for the narrator, right at the beginning of the novel:
We have a word in German: schweigen. *It means deliberately remaining silent; it is different to merely being quiet.*

Or that's the final version, after workshopping the first page with my 'translation lab' in Berlin and after an excellent edit by my esteemed colleague Florian Duijsens. A sentence and a half that took over a year to translate. Sandra was happy with it, I'm happy with it, and I hope you, the reader, perceived it as the right opening to a German book all about deliberate silences.